TALES FROM THE BAZAARS

TALES
FROM THE
BAZAARS

by
Amina Shah

The Octagon Press
London

Requests for permission to reprint, reproduce, etc., to:
Permissions Department, The Octagon Press Ltd.,
P O Box 227, London N6 4EW, England

ISBN 0 863040 84 5

First published in 2002

Printed and bound in Great Britain by
MPG Books Ltd., Bodmin, Cornwall

Contents

Tales from the Bazaars   1

Zorah, the Goldsmith's Daughter   2

The Old One and the Seeker   8

The Bully and the Poisoned Fish   14

The Princess of Fantasistan   18

The Warrior's Daughter and the Four Suitors   23

The Queen of Saba and the Infidel   26

The Caliph's Deception   32

Tales from Turkey   39

Prince Attila's Journey to the End of the World   40

The King, the Dog and the Golden Bowl   47

The Lady Who Came Out of a Cupboard   52

The Poor Bird-catcher and the Talking Bird   62

Tales from Persia   67

Princess Feroza and the Horse Prince   68

The Weaver and the *Dev*   74

The Water-Carrier and the Three Walnuts   75

Rustam and the Iron Fortress   83

The Shah's Ring   88

Amerindian Tales   95

  The Girl of the Great Mountain   96
  Bearwoman and the Little Navajo   101
  Black Bull and the Magic Drum   107
  Golden Eagle's Magic Bag   112
  The Sleeper of the Cave of Darkness   118
  The Three Brothers   123
  The Singing Stones   127
  The Dog and the Bear   132
  The Fair Mohican   139
  The Trail to the West   144

Tales from Arabia   149

  The Tale of Hatim Tai   150
  The Princess, the Vizier and the Ape   155
  The Deaf Brother and the Blind Brother   158
  The Sultan's Emissary and the Leopard   162
  The Faithful Gazelle   169

Tales from India   177

  The Story of the Taj Mahal   178
  The Man who Made Gold   181
  The Young Ant   186
  The Miser and the Generous Man   187
  The Story of the Koh-i-Noor   193
  The King who Had Everything   196
  The Meatball's Fate   199
  The Emerald Scorpion   201

Romany Tales   **209**

    The Story of Carrot Top   210
    The Silver Ring of Black Lopez   219
    The Mayfly   223
    The Magic Peg Basket   225
    The Romany who Married a Bird Woman   231
    The Romany who Talked to Animals   237

Tales from Afghanistan   **241**

    The Emir's Cook and the Unforgettable Sneeze   242
    The Magnificent Boots   245
    The Prince who Feared Tigers   251
    The Pebble which Wanted to Travel the World   264
    The Lost Mares   271
    The Precious Pearl   275
    The Treasure Hoard of the *Afreet*   279
    The Nagging Grandmother   286
    The Girl with the Glass Heart   292
    The Keeper of the King's Horses   301
    The Magic Talisman   304
    The Game of 'I Remember'   311
    The Carpet Merchant's Daughter and the Snake   314
    Abdul Karim's Escape   323

❧ TALES FROM THE BAZAARS ❧

Zorah, the Goldsmith's Daughter

THERE WAS ONCE a goldsmith who made such exquisite jewellery that his name was known far and wide. In all the bazaars of Damascus there was no work more excellent than his. His fame was so great that one day the Prince of Darkness himself, the evil Eblis, came to look at his wares.

The goldsmith was sitting at his bench, putting the finishing touches to a magnificent necklace for a lady of high degree to wear at her wedding, when he saw the dark, wicked face of the Satanic prince looking at the display of wonderful gem-studded treasures. The horns on the Evil One's head immediately told the goldsmith who his client was, and he cried out as the tall, black-robed figure entered the shop, 'Oh, have mercy upon me, great Prince of Darkness! Has my last hour come, then?'

The Evil One smiled and replied, 'Have no fear of me at this time, O most excellent goldsmith. I have not come to carry you off. I had heard of your remarkable workmanship and had a wish to see it for myself. What delightful things you have in the window here, to be sure!'

'Please, please take anything you wish, with my compliments,' cried the goldsmith. 'There are some of the finest gold chains in the world here, jewelled fish with ruby eyes, a golden elephant with jade tusks, a ring set with five emeralds.' The jeweller was so delighted at not being taken to the lower regions that he would have given away anything that the Evil One wanted, out of sheer relief.

'Oh no, no! I don't want them now,' said the Prince of Darkness. 'Keep them for me and I will come back for them when I am ready.'

'Everything is yours, everything,' the goldsmith rattled on, 'all that there is in the window.'

'All right, everything in the window, then. Keep them for me and I will come and collect them sometime. Remember, I may not want them for years but when I do, I shall expect you to keep your promise, or else!'

'I promise,' said the goldsmith, and the tall, black-robed figure disappeared as suddenly as sheet lightning, leaving behind a faint smell of sulphur. The goldsmith rushed behind the shop to his wife.

'My dear, quick, help me to put all these things out of the window into a box. You will never guess who wants them — Eblis the Evil One. He was here just now and has made me promise to keep everything for him until he returns.'

'Everything in the window?!' his wife shrieked.

'Yes, yes. But luckily he hadn't come for me, don't you realise? He went off quite satisfied, I think.'

'Oh, you fool, husband,' she cried. 'Look! Our little daughter is in the window, playing with those golden ear-rings, and there's no doubt the Evil One means to have her too.'

The goldsmith rushed to look; sure enough he saw his beloved baby daughter, Zorah, playing there.

'Quickly, wife,' he said, 'go to the silversmith and bring me back an ounce of virgin silver.'

The woman did as she was told and soon the goldsmith was hammering out a circle of silver. Upon it he engraved a secret, sacred verse from the Koran to protect his child from the machinations of the evil Prince of Darkness. He and his wife asked the Mullah to sprinkle it with holy water from the well of Zam Zam, and it was tied around the little girl's neck on a silken thread. Little Zorah was told she that she must never take it from her neck or the Evil One would carry her away.

Years passed and still the Satanic visitor had not returned. The goldsmith and his wife had forgotten the whole incident when suddenly the Evil One appeared again in the shop.

'I've come for my treasure,' he said. 'Remember your promise? The girl is now seventeen years old, is she not?'

'Oh, great Prince of Darkness,' wept the goldsmith, 'spare her, spare her please! Take me, but leave my dear Zorah in the world to enjoy her life, I beg you.'

By now his wife had appeared and she fell to her knees, adding her prayers. But the Evil One was in a great rage and bellowed at them to bring out their daughter as he, Eblis, hadn't got all day and was anxious to return to the lower regions, where he had work of great importance.

Hearing the noise in the shop, Zorah came in and with all the innocence of her years smiled charmingly at the tall Prince of Darkness, fingering her magic talisman as she did so.

'Oh, very well, then,' scowled the Evil One, who was both captivated by her beauty and anxious to appear wonderful in her sight. 'I will give you seven more days with your parents, my dear. After that I really must return and claim you as my bride.' And with that, he vanished in a puff of smoke.

Now the goldsmith had a plan and it was this: he would make a life-sized wax model of his daughter, cleverly concealing a machine inside the figure so that it could walk and talk like a live human being. He spent days and nights working on the doll. By the time the Evil One was due to return, a beautiful reproduction of his daughter, scented and veiled, was concealed behind a silken curtain awaiting the devilish bridegroom. When the Satanic prince reappeared he was in a bad temper again and he said, 'Come now, old man, give me your daughter or I will send some of my fiends to burn this place to the ground!'

Looking towards the curtain the goldsmith said, 'Come, Zorah my child, here is the mighty Eblis, Prince of Darkness, to take you to his kingdom below. Hasten, and go with him with all speed.' And pulling the beautiful life-sized doll towards him, the goldsmith took from around its neck the protective silver talisman which had prevented the Evil One from touching his daughter. He put it on top of the cupboard in which his real daughter was concealed from view.

The curtains parted, the doll came walking forward fluttering her eyelashes provocatively, and the Evil One seized the lovely creature and bore her away below. Once in his own realm, the deluded Eblis placed her upon a fantastic throne. It was decorated with wonderful jewels and he was eager to show off his kingdom of fire.

That night there was to be a banquet in celebration of

the Evil One's new bride. The Satanic minions were instructed to place the lovely Zorah at the right hand of the Prince of Darkness, in the great dining hall of the palace of eternal flames. Wine was brought in gleaming goblets for the excited Eblis. He was delighted when the doll kept turning her head towards him and smiling, appearing to admire his every word. The minions piled more and more coal on the fire. The wine flowed, food was brought, and the Evil One was in his element, enjoying himself enormously and anticipating joys to come.

Suddenly, the lovely wax maiden began to wilt. As the fiends put more fuel on the flames, the doll fell forward into the fire. Within a few seconds, it was consumed and there was not one scrap left of the beautiful creature. The fiends stood aghast. How were they going to tell their master of this turn of events? How would he take his loss? What would happen to them for their carelessness? They leaned on their pitchforks, their eyes almost bulging out of their heads, their hoofs red-hot, their tails twitching with anxiety. Still the Prince of Darkness drank and ate and exchanged quips with those guests especially chosen by him to share the banquet. He had noticed nothing.

Finally, one fiend, braver than the rest, went and whispered in the Evil One's left ear. 'What,' cried he, 'fell in the fire and was burned? Well, these human beings are a hopeless lot! She'd only just arrived. I must have been mad to think she could have lasted down here for all eternity as my princess. Go, make the fires even hotter. We will enjoy ourselves tonight!'

And so the party of all those damned souls became

merrier and merrier. The wine glasses were refilled, each plate was replenished often and the food heaped high. And Eblis, the Prince of Darkness, never thought of Zorah, the goldsmith's daughter, ever again.

The Old One and the Seeker

*T*HE SHEIKH WITH THE brown camel-hair robe and the white head-dress wound around his head smiled to himself in the last flickering flames of the caravanserai fire. He put down his silver water goblet of the finest Syrian design, and said to the assembled company, 'Brothers, if I may be allowed to contribute this tale which I heard from my grandfather when I was young? Very well. It is a tale I have told and retold and I never tire of it. I had best begin at the beginning:

'Once there was a young man who wanted above all to travel to a cave at the top of a certain mountain in the high Himalayas. In that cave there dwelt in perfect peace and tranquillity a famous sage known to all as "The Old One".

'The wisdom, knowledge and spiritual perfection of this wise man were said to be without parallel in the world. And Abdullah, such was the seeker's name, made up his mind to conquer the long and dangerous road to the cave of The Old One, hoping to be accepted to study the ancient's philosophy and thereby gain the key to success, the gateway to spiritual power and the strength to over-throw the forces of ignorance. Towards this end, he trained himself in mountain-climbing, accumulated a store of dried fruit and nuts, and set off — young and eager — towards his goal.

'His parents saw how he had made this visit the most important thing in his life and neither father nor mother sought to dissuade him. Their prayers and blessings sent him on his way as he walked away, up towards the horizon.

'It was spring, and the fragile flowers which grew all around lifted Abdullah's spirits whenever he felt despondent. The wild birds cheered him with their musical cries. His feet, as sure as a goat's, sought each crevice; every finger-hold strong enough to bear him helped him rise higher and higher until, finally, he came to a round, smooth, rocky throne at the entrance to The Old One's cave. The light on the mountainside was extremely bright, and there in the brilliant glow sat The Old One, apparently incandescent with the wisdom of the ages. His body was spare, and his clothes were the same colour as the mountain rocks; his hair was as white as the snow on the mountain top, and his eyes were a dark, glittering black in his parchment face. Leaning back on the stony throne, the Old One glanced at Abdullah with no more welcome or interest than if the youth were a gnat or a stone on the hillside.

'Stumbling and falling, and picking himself up again, Abdullah at last threw himself at The Old One's feet, breathless and excited at finally having arrived and with an expectation of instant illumination. He began with his autobiographical details as soon as he was moderately comfortable, propping himself on his battered knees — and then he told of his great desire to see and listen to The Old One. From being pale and untroubled, The Old One's face turned red and angry. He pointed down the mountain path the way the youth had come and cried out: "Go!"

'Abdullah began to beg and pray, "Take me on as your

pupil, please. I'll stay as long as it takes to learn. I want to find the way. Please, please, Old One, don't turn me away, hungry and thirsty as I am for knowledge and wisdom. Have pity!"

'The old man got up, as smoothly as an agile animal, and from a leather satchel in the shadow of the throne, extracted some dried fruit, nuts and a flask of fresh water. These he offered to the unhappy Abdullah, inviting him to eat and drink. Then he pointed for the second time to the path below and said, "Go!"

'He lowered himself onto his throne once more and sat, contemplating the far, far whiteness of the everlasting snows while the would-be disciple ate and drank. Then, at a sign from The Old One, he put the rest of the food into his own empty satchel and asked: "Have you no message for me? I made this long journey to fulfill my dream of seeing you. Please guide me in the way to live my life and teach me to help others to succeed, as I hope to succeed after I've been trained by you."

'The glittering black eyes met Abdullah's tear-stung ones. They were not unkindly now, just penetrating, and seemed to sear into Abdullah's soul. For the third time the thin, bony, beautifully formed fingers of The Old One's hand pointed back the way the young man had come.

'"I repeat my words to you — go, go, go. Make use of them as you will."

'The eyes of jet were lost in folds of grey skin as The Old One's eyelids closed, in apparent sleep.

'Abdullah was dismissed.

'He climbed down and down, back the way he had

come. When the way got too difficult he rested, but before the light failed completely, he was back on the trail he knew: the foothills of the Himalayas near his home. Finishing the last of The Old One's dried fruits and nuts, he refreshed himself with water springing from a rock, and went on with his loping hill-man's stride. As the full moon rose and helped him home, he felt less downhearted and even sang a few snatches of song to himself as he walked. Somehow he felt more energised than he had ever been before, by the very fact of having seen The Old One.

'When he returned home so quickly, though his parents were naturally delighted, his mother plied him with questions. "What did you learn from The Old One, my son?" she asked. "What did he say? What have you learned? Tell us, omitting no detail."

'"I must go," said the beardless Abdullah. "Now I have seen him and heard his instructions, I must go."

'"Go where, dear Abdullah?" shrieked his mother. "Go? Go? Go where, what do you mean? Leave us? Leave this village of sixty-four souls? Explain yourself, Abdullah. What has The Old One told you to do?"

'"He told me to go, to go away and go quickly," said Abdullah firmly.

'He had a good night's sleep in his old home, and then with a few items necessary for the journey and the clothes he stood up in, he bade his parents goodbye and walked away to seek his fortune.

'Now Abdullah was not trained in anything, having spent most of his youth helping his family to farm the small strip of land they lived upon. In the first town to which he came, there was plenty of work for young, willing hands in the building of the sultan's palace, and in the planting of its gardens. As he grew more experienced at his work, he earned more money and was thus able to travel further to great cities and beautiful towns. Each time he pondered in his mind as to what action might be safest, The Old One's words came to him immediately as the right course of action to take:

'"Go."

'He worked his way through many countries and, after some years, people he worked with began to value his experience of the world and would ask him questions to which, after waiting a few minutes to summon the face of The Old One before him, he would answer, "Go".

'So they went ahead with the project which they were dithering about, or just pulled up their tent poles and went away elsewhere. In each case when they had the courage to do this, they were pleased with the result of the move. Abdullah got the reputation of being somewhat of a wise man himself, even without thinking about the advice he was giving.

'At last, middle-aged and tired of all that life had so far given him, he had come to feel that he was the rolling stone which gathers no moss, and he decided to head for home. He had no wife and no family — his parents had died by the time he returned to his village. And all the women who had been girls when he was young, were now married.

'Wondering what to do next, the grey-haired Abdullah one day found himself climbing up the path he had taken as a young man towards the cave of The Old One. Would the cave still be there? Would the old man still be alive? Had he really seen that ancient sage and heard those three words, "Go, go, go"? Or was it all in his imagination?

'There was nothing to do but climb up and find out. He longed with all his heart and all his mind to reach that enchanted spot. His feet took him unerringly to the very place. He saw the same rocky throne and the slight figure of The Old One, who was there in his robes of fluttering material. The glittering black eyes were now full of bright welcome.

'Abdullah stood in humble pride before the master and spoke not a word, his head held high. His gaze did not falter. The Old One rose as nimbly as a boy, and pointed with an inviting hand towards the cave of a thousand books of knowledge.

'"I said *Go* to you before," said The Old One softly, taking him by the arm. "Now my instruction is different. Now I say to you, *Come*."'

The Bully and the Poisoned Fish

ONCE UPON A TIME not so long ago, there was a fishing village on the edge of the ocean. Every morning the legions of fishermen would hurry ashore with their catch. They worked hard and endured rough seas in their fragile boats, but the haul was always good. All the villagers were content, and almost everyone was everyone else's friend but at one end of the village there lived a bully. He was a huge, ugly fellow with a great head, rolling eyes which never seemed to stay still, large flat feet pointing east and west, and a loud, grating voice. He was always twisting other men's arms, pulling the girls' hair, tripping women carrying baskets of fish from the boats. Not a day went by without him making a nuisance of himself.

Every day, he would challenge some male villager to a wrestling match and most of them good-naturedly wrestled with him. But unless they were careful, he would throw his opponent to the ground very heavily and then sit on him until he begged for mercy. When each in turn had acknowledged him as the undisputed winner and the strongest man in the whole district, he would jump up and down and crow like a demented rooster, thumping his chest as if he were an orang-utan. His cudgel, the local weapon, was a brutal thing, but he loved to use it. Over time, he got more and more difficult to reason with, and became quite impossible to talk to. Everyone in the village had their own cudgel but he always won, no matter whom he challenged.

Now, on the day of which I speak, a small, slim, brown-skinned stranger came to the headman of the village. He asked for shelter for the night, explaining that he was a student on a walking pilgrimage to the high caves of the bats, in the jungle far inland.

Every villager was happy to have a new face in the village and they each brought a dish of fish or spiced rice to the headman's house so that the visitor could be shown the customary hospitality with a feast on the beach.

The evening was well advanced and all had eaten and drunk well, when a huge, squat figure rose from the ranks of seated villagers, and challenged the visitor to a fight. The mild-mannered, slim stranger got calmly to his feet and, as the villagers watched with dismay, a space was cleared for the contest to begin. The bully's cudgel was ready.

'I am not much good at cudgelling,' said the visitor. 'I usually fight with wet fish as my weapon. As I am the challenged person, naturally I get the choice of weapons, don't I?'

'Oh, certainly, certainly, I can use a wet fish as a weapon as easily as a cudgel,' said the bully, 'and I am ready to start. Where are the two fish we are to use?'

Eagerly, the men of the village began speculating as to how much they should wager and on which contestant.

'I have them here in my knapsack,' replied the stranger, 'and the sooner we start the betting the better, for I usually have a wet fish fight wherever I go, and have won nearly all of them. The thing is, one of these two fish is poisoned and you must choose which one you will use as a weapon against me. Taking the wrong one could be fatal, for there's a secret poison under the scales. As your hands close around the tail of the fish to give me a heavy enough blow, there could be a risk of the poison coming in contact with your skin. Of course it might be I who takes the poisoned fish — we do not know which is which. But I'm sure you're sportsman enough to give little thought to which is the poisoned fish and which is not. Come on, make your choice and we will get this over with once and for all, and then these good folk may go their separate ways.'

He held out the palm leaf satchel which had been hanging at his side. All who could craned their heads forward to see two strange-looking, long-bodied fish — the colour of red mullet and with red-rimmed eyes — lying in the satchel. There was not so much as a frightened whisper in the crowd. The children were hushed and the headman's brow grew wet with sweat. Nobody moved; they just squatted where they were, watching the confrontation between the big ugly bully and the small slim visitor with the mild manner.

'You mean we're only going to fight with fish instead of cudgels?' shouted the bully, his eyes bulging. A look that the villagers recognised as pure cowardice came over his face. 'Why, I'm not going to have anything to do with a contest like that. It's beneath me! You can do that sort of thing in the stupid towns where you come from, but not in this village, you know. I'm not going to take the risk of getting poisoned in a stupid game like that. Huh!'

And he turned on his heel and disappeared in the

direction of his own hut. For the first time, he had been thwarted. Never again would he dare to challenge anyone else.

A buzz of excited conversation began, as the fish were put back into the satchel and people began eating the rest of the succulent dishes laid out on the beach. Women laughed, men smoked, children giggled and ran about.

'A delightful day, indeed. I shall be glad to settle down to sleep,' said the mild-mannered visitor to the relieved headman. 'I want to thank you very much indeed for your delicious food and entertaining conversation. Please accept these two fish from the island next to this. They may have a different flavour to your own local catches,' continued the young man, pushing the palm leaf satchel towards the bewildered headman's hand with a gentle and encouraging smile.

'But, but what do you mean? You said that one of them was poisoned!' spluttered the headman, beginning to sweat profusely again. 'How can you do this to us after all our kindness and our hospitality?'

'No, no, please have the fish. Grill one for breakfast, boil them, eat them raw. They will be delicious any way. Neither one of them has poison on the tail. That was just my little joke. But your village bully doesn't know that, so he'll never trouble you again.'

The Princess of Fantasistan

'*I*N THE WHOLE LAND of Turkistan,' began the merchant from Bokhara, 'there was never — believe me, my brothers — a lady more beautiful and kind than the Princess of Fantasistan.'

'Fantasistan!? Fantasistan?!' cried the carpet-seller from Mazar-i-Sharif. 'But in my language that means fantasy-land or nowhere, an invention.'

'Exactly,' smiled the dreamy-eyed Bokharan, adjusting the skirts of his padded coat of many colours. 'I will tell you all about her if you want to hear me out.'

The other merchants settled down, each on his elbow around the fire. Servants threw more wood on the flames and the story began:

'In the land of Turkistan, there was once this most beautiful and exceedingly kind princess. The King of Turkistan had met her one day when he was out hunting, and the moment he set eyes upon her gathering berries, dressed in the simplest of garments, he fell in love with her. He was young and bold and looking for a suitable princess to choose as his wife, but up until that moment no woman had ever stirred his pulse as this one did.

'He enquired as to her parents' whereabouts so that he could ask for her hand, but she shook her head every time he asked her. The eyes she raised to his were as pure and childlike as pools of water. She appeared to be quite alone in the world. So he lifted her upon his horse and happily took her to the blue turquoise palace where he lived with his mother and sisters. With great ceremony, dressed in fine coloured silk wedding garments and with a magnificent head-dress of silver and cornelian, the lovely creature was married to the young King of Turkistan.

'All was well for a year and the courtiers soon found that their new queen was merry and kind and sweet and joyful. Her little son, the prince, born to the couple after nine months of marriage, was now three months old. But the King's three sisters, as yet unmarried themselves, were becoming increasingly jealous of her.

'They started rumours about her — first in the court and then far and wide across the whole country of Turkistan, putting the question in everyone's mind, "Who is this girl who has married our noble ruler? Is she really worthy? What will her children be like? How is it that the King has been so foolish as to bring us back a queen from a hunting expedition — someone about whom we know nothing?"

'Those who loved her defended her, saying, "She must be of good family and a fit mother for our ruler's children. Look at her, can you not see it in her face?"

'"Let us go to her native country then," screamed the malcontents in the pay of the evil princesses. "Take us back to this fantasyland, this Fantasistan from whence she comes, and let us see it for ourselves."

'"The people really hate me," thought the poor young queen. "I will never be able to satisfy them. My sisters-in-law are evil and cruel."

'Every day the rumours grew more and more ugly. In the end she thought, "The King will be happier without me. I had better go away — back to where he found me. At least I was happy there, living on berries and fruit, and I had my happy memories of things past."

'So when the King and his party next set out hunting, she wrapped up the little prince in a warm blanket, took a few things in a bag, and went off as fast as she could in the opposite direction.

'Now the courtiers, most of whom opposed her, followed at a distance to see where she went. They feared she might be just a beggar girl who had trapped their King into marriage, and they were anxious to find out the whole truth of the matter.

'When she arrived at the wood where, a year before, she had been gathering berries, she went quickly in through the trees and sank down. To the amazement of all, there, in the clearing behind her, stood a most fantastic palace, as big as that of the King of Turkistan. There were glittering jewels set into white alabaster domes, doorways of carved ivory, silver cages with singing birds in them and fighting quail in reed baskets. There were deer in the gardens and flowers of great beauty growing all round the walls. Tall, handsome soldiers in shining armour and steel helmets guarded the gates and walked up and down in great numbers.

'The tired young queen in her dusty robes, with the little prince in her arms, rose again and limped towards the gate. Silver trumpets immediately pealed out a greeting as she came and pennants fluttered from the balconies. People appeared at the windows to wave a welcome. A tall white-haired, queenly figure and a noble old King came out of the palace saying, "Oh come in, dear one! Come in, come in, dear long-lost daughter. What kept you from coming to us? Bring in your friends who are there behind you. Let no one be forgotten. Let food be brought and let them be given beautiful presents."

'To their surprise, the courtiers were taken into the palace by a great crowd of happy, smiling people. There, they were seated on sofas and fed and fanned by many slaves, and the festivities continued for seven days and seven nights.

'On the second night, the King of Turkistan, back from his hunting trip, went looking for his wife. The way she had gone was pointed out to him by courtiers who had been the scandal-mongers' confidantes but who had remained behind to look after the Turkistani palace.

'When the King reached the palace in the wood, the tall queen and her husband introduced themselves as the King and Queen of Fantasistan. They embraced their new son-in-law tenderly, played with the little prince, and professed themselves satisfied with their daughter's new life.

'As the courtiers saw their young queen to be truly of noble blood, they all made their excuses and shamefacedly drifted away. How had they come to doubt the choice of their King?

'The queen-mother said to the young man, "Go to your courtiers and leave our beloved daughter with us here for one more night. We shall send her back to you safely with the little prince, never fear."

'So they went off, with many a backward glance at the palace of the kingdom of Fantasistan. The young queen went to bed that night happy and content, with her child sleeping beside her.

'In the morning all was gone. The palace, the old white-haired queen, the tall King, slaves, soldiers, birds, flowers — nothing was left — not one stick, not one stone. As the girl got to her feet and lifted the child onto her hip and looked around, the old Queen appeared to her again. "Your dear father and I died and became ghosts many years ago," she said, "and the woodcutters' and foresters' families fed you and clothed you until it was your fate to meet the King of Turkistan. But when we saw that you were being so cruelly persecuted, we came back from the World of Worlds to help you. We were granted just seven days and seven nights by Allah, the Merciful, and in that time we could have everything the world can offer. This I share with you, dearest daughter. Bless you, my child, goodbye." And she vanished again, forever.'

The Warrior's Daughter
and the Four Suitors

ONCE UPON A TIME there lived a brave and noble warrior who fought many battles for the great Saladin. When he became too old to fight, he and his wife went to their own village and lived a rural life. They had one child, a beautiful daughter called Zulaikha, as fair as any girl in the world. She was as good as she was lovely, with bewitching black eyes and a slim figure as supple as a willow wand.

When she was of marriageable age, her parents were happy to receive proposals from many handsome young men. One day, four brothers came all together to seek her hand. The old warrior was very amused at the appearance of the four young brothers, each certain that he would be the lucky one. They all sat in the courtyard of the father's house as Zulaikha and her mother, veiled and hidden from the men's eyes, sat on the balcony above.

'Why should my daughter become your wife?' was the father's question of the first brother, who was handsome and elegant, and a weaver by trade.

'Because I will give your daughter the finest stuffs, made of silk and wool, embroidered and fine,' said the weaver. 'She will never lack for wonderful clothes and she will be the most beautifully dressed girl in the whole of the country.'

'And why should my daughter become your wife?' was the question to the second brother, who was also handsome and elegant.

'Because I am skilled in the knowledge of all animals and birds — I will teach your daughter the language of the wild creatures. I will take her to the forests and the woods and show her their homes, and I will dress her in the finest of their furs.'

Then spoke the father to the third suitor. 'Why should my daughter become your wife?'

'Because I am a poet and a writer and I will be able to immortalise her beauty and tell her wonderful stories every night of her life. I will read her wondrous tales from many lands.'

'And why do you want to marry my daughter?' asked the father of the fourth suitor.

'Oh noble warrior, I want to marry your daughter because I am a warrior and you are a warrior. I will give your daughter many sons who will also be brave fighting men, and I will give your daughter daughters who can be the wives of warriors. As my blood is of your blood, I will shed it for our country and our name, and I will make you proud of your grandchildren, O noble warrior,' said the fourth young man.

'You must take my daughter,' said the old warrior, 'for you have spoken as I myself spoke to her mother when I went to take her hand. For like must go with like, eagle with eagle and pigeon with pigeon.'

At that moment a golden scarf fell from the balcony above onto the shoulders of the brave young warrior.

He looked up and met the eyes of the daughter of the old warrior.

And so it must be as Allah has willed. Like must go to like — scribes must marry the daughters of scribes and warriors must marry the daughters of warriors.

The Queen of Saba and the Infidel

*I*N THE COUNTRY OF HADHRAMAUT, which means Danger of Death, there was a great queen, Bilqis, Queen of Saba. She was a very clever woman, and had been on a long journey to see Suleiman, the King of the Magicians. After visiting the wise King, she returned to her own land blessed with much knowledge.

One day her guards brought an Englishman to her court and threw him down in front of the queen: 'O great Queen Bilqis,' they said, 'we have found this infidel wandering near your palace. We can get no truth out of him. He is pale and so thin, and has little of the beautiful Arabic of our land on his tongue. So before we behead him or throw him to the lions, we would like you to see this strange creature.'

Now Bilqis was only a woman and she was very attracted to this strange, pale, blue-eyed foreigner. She said to them, 'Stop! Do not take his life. What has he done except come here?'

'He has done no evil, O Queen, but he has dared to profane the streets of Saba with his infidel presence.'

The queen spoke to the Englishman and said, 'Stand up. Why are you here?'

He said, 'O great Queen, I have heard of you from many people who have been through the land of the Danger of Death. They said that you were wise and that you were beautiful — I can see from looking at you that they were right.'

The Queen was very flattered and said, 'Sit down. My people may tear you to pieces or throw you to the lions, but I would like to talk to you and ask you: What is it that you infidels do in your country and what do you believe in? Do you not want to embrace our wonderful religion and become one of the jewels of Islam?'

And he replied, 'No, oh Queen, I have made my own arrangements and I have made my peace with my own God.'

'But,' she said, 'you must listen to what my wise men have to say and you must talk and study with them. If you do this properly, perhaps I will let you go.'

'No, great Queen, I would rather be put to death than change my religion,' said the infidel.

Then the Queen cried, 'Well said! I am glad to hear that. We've been told by our book that people who have another book are also to be honoured. Do you have a book?'

'Yes, great Queen, we have a book.'

'Good, ' she said. 'Then you shall come hunting with me today and walk with me in the garden tonight. You will eat with me and my people and I will put questions to you. You shall listen to the wisdom I have learned from the great King Suleiman.'

So the days and the nights passed very well for Bilqis, Queen of Saba, and she enjoyed the company of the Englishman. He, in his way, enjoyed the company of the Queen. But he didn't like the way the courtiers looked at him out of the corners of their eyes, and sensed great hostility from them. He felt jealousies had arisen and that soon he would have to make his way from the Land of Hadhramaut, which means Danger of Death.

One night the Queen gave a great feast and there were many people there. They all came to look at the Englishman and to watch the way he spoke to their Queen. And the green-eyed monster of jealousy came into the heart of her Grand Vizier. He leaned across and whispered something to the Englishman. The Englishman didn't catch it, so he said, 'What? Would you say that again? What do you mean? I don't understand.'

The Grand Vizier became very angry and said, 'You don't understand, you don't understand! I've just said something to you of great importance and you don't understand? O Queen, listen to this fool. He must go immediately to the dungeons. We can't have any more of him. He said something very wrong about you.'

And so the Queen lost her temper too and said, 'Take him away to the dungeons.'

'No, no!' cried the Englishman. 'This is all a mistake. The Grand Vizier has misunderstood.'

The Queen said, 'Very well, then. I'll give you one more chance.'

She cast about in her mind and then said, 'If, in your country, you have learned everything and know everything, then I would like you to bring me the answer to this riddle tomorrow. You must stay in the dungeon until this time tomorrow and when you return you must bring me the answer.'

'Very well, what is the question?' asked the Englishman.

'The question is,' said the queen, 'Where is the centre of the world? I'll put it in another way — which is the most important place in this universe? Now take him away!' With that she gave a wave of her hand, and her guards leapt forward and dragged the poor Englishman away.

He was taken to a cell in the very darkest part of the palace and locked up. There was no light and he lay on the floor in great agony of mind. Why had he stayed so long in this crazy city of Saba? Why had he not skirted the great desert of Hadhramaut, because now he was certainly going to have his head cut off. By this time tomorrow he would surely have met his maker. He lay on the floor and beat his hands in agony upon a huge stone that was flattened and scratched with the names of people who had obviously been incarcerated there before him.

Suddenly he was aware that the darkness of the cell was no more. A bright light came from the stone upon which he had beaten with his clenched fists. There issued from it a voice saying, 'Oh human being, I am a magic stone. Ask of me anything you wish to know and I will answer. This is a talismanic stone upon which you have beaten your hand, and we, the *jinn* of the stone must answer your question.'

'Then for God's sake,' said the Englishman, 'for God's sake, magic stone, can you tell me the answer to this: What is the centre of the world? What is the very middle of the universe? What is the answer to the question that the Queen of Saba has asked?'

He put his ear to the stone and the stone whispered to him. Then the voice in the stone said, 'Have you heard this, O Infidel?'

And he said, 'Yes, I've heard it.'

'Then tell it to the Queen and may peace be upon you.'

'Upon you too be peace,' cried the unfortunate Englishman.

The light went out. There was darkness and he heard and saw no more. He was so relieved by what he had been told that he lay down upon the hard cell floor and slept.

In the early dawn they woke him, took him out, washed him, gave him food, dressed him in clean clothes and walked him through the palace. At last he arrived at the Queen's throne.

The Queen said, 'What is the answer to my question? What is the centre of the universe? What is the most important spot in the whole world?'

All the courtiers looked on and listened. Their eyes were green with envy and their fingers were clenched like claws. They looked forward to what they thought would be the destruction of the terrible infidel, the Englishman, of whom they had become so jealous.

The Englishman stood up very straight and tall, he shook out his cloak, and put one foot forward. He bent his knee, leant forward, smoothed his beard, and said, 'O great Bilqis, Queen of Saba, it lies here at your feet. The most important part of the world is where you are, O great Queen of Hadhramaut.'

The Queen laughed and her eyes lit up. Her counsellors and viziers fell back as she stretched out her hand and took that of the infidel. 'You have spoken well and you shall now go free,' she said, 'and I will give you my finest camel. He will take you beyond Hadhramaut and the Danger of Death and you can go back to your infidel country. Once there, you can tell them of the wisdom and the power of the Queen of Saba and how she has returned an infidel to his infidel land.'

And so the magic stone had saved him from a terrible fate, and the infidel was able to return to his country to set down this tale.

The Caliph's Deception

ONE EVENING, THE CALIPH of Baghdad, Haroun al Rashid, was wandering through the streets of his city, disguised as was his wont, when he saw a man in a tattered cloak lying asleep, huddled against an outdoor oven.

'Jafar,' said the Caliph to his Grand Vizier, who usually accompanied him on journeys like this, 'what a shame that this man should have to lie in the street with no bed under him. Look through his pockets. Has he no money?'

The Vizier searched the man's pockets and found nothing, not a single copper coin. 'He has nothing, Your Highness. He seems to be penniless. Yet there is something about his face that is so calm and fine. He might, dare I say it, even pass for you if he were dressed in fine clothes. It is the most remarkable likeness, forgive me for saying so.'

Haroun al Rashid looked closer and agreed. 'Yes, how remarkable! He certainly has the features of our family — the same type of nose, similar shaped eyebrows.'

He looked thoughtful and Jafar, the Vizier, said, 'Let us put coins in his pocket so that he wakes to a day of prosperity.'

'I have a better idea,' said the Caliph. 'Let us take him to the palace. He seems to be so deeply asleep, as if he would never awaken. We can take him to my own chamber and put him there tonight. Tomorrow we can give him new clothes and see if he needs work.'

So the Caliph and Jafar very gently carried the snoring

man by a secret way to the Caliph's chamber and, pulling off his old cloak, covered him with a silken bedspread. No sooner had they done so than there was a knock at the door.

'Is the Caliph awake? There is grave news from the battlefield.'

It was the commander-in-chief of the Caliph's army. 'Our men are losing heart, Caliph. If they could only see you and be encouraged by you, the infidels could quite easily be routed.'

Haroun al Rashid spoke quickly, 'Wait half an hour and I will be with you, properly accoutred for the fight.'

The General saluted and went away.

The Caliph said, 'Jafar, no one must know I have gone. Keep my departure secret. I must be with my men under our banner. If our enemies knew my movements, they might try to kill me before I can reach our camps.'

'But Your Highness, what of this fellow whom we have just put to bed?' said Jafar. 'He is sleeping so soundly there. He looks likely to sleep until the Day of Judgment.'

'Keep him here. Dress him as myself and tell him what you like but keep him here until I return.'

The Caliph put on his sword and his military cloak and vanished through a secret door in the wall.

'May Allah send the Caliph victory,' murmured the faithful Jafar, and scratched his head as he kept watch by the bed of the beggar.

When the man, whose name was Abdullah, woke in the early morning, he could not believe the evidence of his own eyes. Here he was in a great room, in a bed the like of which he had never seen in all his born days, and covered with a silken bedspread! His head was aching, his senses were confused. He sat up wondering what it was all about.

Discreetly, Jafar coughed. 'Ahem — what are your instructions, great Caliph Haroun al Rashid?' he asked. 'You've not been well of late and the doctors have said you should rest. But if you are feeling better, perhaps you would like to be bathed, Caliph.'

'Caliph, Caliph! I'm not a Caliph. I'm a poor man who has been looking for work all week long, and finding none nor any likelihood of it, I fell asleep from exhaustion in the street last night — or at least I think it was last night. My wife and children are waiting for me at home. I must go.'

'No, no, no, you've been ill. There's nothing you can do about these fantasies, Your Highness,' said Jafar, and very soothingly he talked until Abdullah began to feel he must be the Caliph. He allowed himself to be bathed and dressed and fed with delicious food, for he was weak with hunger and dizzy with confusing thoughts.

'If this is all in my imagination,' he reasoned, 'and I am mad, how agreeable it is, and who am I to worry if life is so pleasant?' So he went with the tide, allowing things to happen to him.

After a few days, he began to feel as if he really were the ruler who had been ill. Poverty had been a dream. When people sent petitions to him, he read them sympathetically. A poor woman wrote to say that her husband had gone to look for work, had not returned, and that she feared he might have died of hunger on the streets of Baghdad. Immediately, the beggar sent a messenger with a bag of gold, for somehow her words struck him very forcibly.

'Here am I in this wonderful palace, and this poor woman has nothing. The queen in this fabulous court says she is my wife but as I have been ill she wishes to leave me to recover before she visits me. All I have to do is receive the petitions of the people and help as many as I can. Somehow I understand how they feel, so I must be a Caliph.'

Abdullah's wife was delighted with the gold and thanked Allah for his mercy. But she still blamed Abdullah for leaving her and the children. 'Deserting us in our need,' she muttered. 'I wouldn't care if he never came back. He would never have got as much money as this for us in the whole of his life!'

And she bought new clothes for herself and the family.

Meanwhile, the real Caliph led his army to victory and then returned to Baghdad when everything was peaceful again. He came to his room by the hidden door and there was the false Caliph lying asleep. Silently Haroun al Rashid went to Jafar's room and woke him.

'Victory is ours, Jafar. Now I only want sleep and plenty of it until this tiredness has left me,' he said.

'Thanks be to Allah that Your Highness has returned safe and victorious,' responded the Vizier. 'But what are we to do with the man whom the people imagine to be the Caliph? Now he really thinks he is you.'

'He must go back to where we found him,' said the weary ruler. 'Put his tattered cloak around him. Let a couple of men carry him to the same spot and put a bag of gold in a belt around his waist. He is sleeping so soundly, he would not wake if a herd of elephants appeared.'

So the Vizier did as the Caliph had commanded and

at dawn Abdullah woke beside the warm oven by the baker's shop. Instead of the soft bed, there was the hard road under him.

'By Allah,' he cried. 'I knew it was all a dream. Here I am in the street with only my tattered cloak around me. But, wait, what is this belt? Gold? Wait until my wife hears about this!'

And he got up and ran home as fast as he possibly could.

The maidservant was astonished when she opened the door. She cried, 'A miracle, a miracle! My master, are you safe and well? The mistress gave you up for dead a week ago.'

Abdullah went to his wife's bed and showed her the gold.

'Allah be praised,' she wept. 'I thought you had deserted us and I had to appeal to the Caliph. But how did you fare? Where were you? What were you doing? How did you get this money?'

He scratched his head and blinked his eyes, trying hard to remember. 'I cannot be sure what happened to me, my dear,' he said. 'I think I must have been carried away by a *jinn*. I do hope this money is real, for I just couldn't bear it if I were to wake up from this dream.'

And do you know, he never did.

❧ TALES FROM TURKEY ❧

Prince Attila's Journey
to the End of the World

ONCE UPON A TIME there was a King who had a son called Attila. One day he called all his wise men together and said to them, 'How can I test my son to see if he is really brave enough and worthy to be King after me?'

One of the advisers said, 'Send him away to find the magic garden where the Apples of Life grow and bring one back for your Majesty.'

Another said, 'Send him to find the Ring of True Happiness.'

A third said, 'The Prince must bring back the Mirror of Truth from the palace of King Mendoza who lives in the kingdom at the end of the world.'

So the King dismissed his courtiers and sent for his son. When Attila came before him he said, 'My boy, as a test for you, I want you to go out into the world and bring back an apple from the Garden of Life, the Ring of True Happiness, and the Mirror of Truth from the kingdom at the end of the world.'

Prince Attila agreed to go and look for these marvellous things and the King gave a great feast in honour of his son's departure.

That night the Prince lay tossing and turning on his bed wondering how he was going to fare on such a strange journey. Suddenly a bright light shone in the corner of his bedroom and there, in the middle of it, stood a glowing fairy form.

'Do not fear me,' said the dazzling creature. 'I am your fairy guardian and I'm here to help you, Attila. Your father has set you three tasks.'

Attila sat up in bed and stared, unable to speak in his amazement.

'These tasks are not nearly as difficult as you think,' continued the fairy. 'Sleep well tonight and tomorrow when you set off I shall guard you.'

The fairy smiled and put into his hand a magic talisman on a silver chain. 'Put this round your neck, Attila, and when you have need of me rub it three times.' Before Attila was able to thank her, she was gone.

Next morning the Prince rode out of the castle yard with a great sense of excitement, for he had never been out of his father's kingdom before and the whole world lay before him.

He rode on and on, and the fairy's voice came to him whenever he needed to know which way to go. For three days he rode, sleeping beside his horse when darkness came. At last, he came to a strange country and saw a great walled garden in a valley. He galloped on until he came to a huge wrought-iron gate in the wall of the garden which opened when he touched it. He fastened his horse's reins to the gate and wandered among the apple trees which bore fruit on every branch. As he looked about him the voice of his fairy guardian came once more to his ears:

'Take one of the apples, Attila. This is the magic garden where the Apples of Life grow.' He reached up and picked an apple with bright red cheeks. Instantly, a thousand little flying creatures buzzed around him angrily, stinging his hands, his face and his neck. He rubbed the talisman and cried, 'Help! Help!' Immediately the tiny creatures disappeared and all his stings stopped hurting.

Quickly jumping into the saddle, Attila rode and rode until the magic garden lay far behind. Only then did he breathe a sigh of relief. He had got through the first test and the Apple of Life was in his pocket.

Now he was riding through the most beautiful scenery, with flowering blossoms everywhere and a silver stream flowing between mossy banks. He jumped down to have a drink from the stream and his horse slaked its thirst as well. As the horse began to eat the juicy green grass, the Prince began to feel very hungry.

Three pretty village girls came along with baskets of washing which they were soon spreading on the shrubs to dry. When they saw the Prince, they each dropped him a curtsey.

'Can you tell me where I could find lodging for the night?' asked Prince Attila, 'for my horse and I are very tired.'

The youngest girl took him up the hill and showed him a farm house where he could stay for a while. That night, when the farmer and his wife and the Prince were sitting around the kitchen table at their evening meal, there came a knock at the door.

'Who could that be at this time of the night?' said the farmer as he went to answer the door. A poor old beggar man stood there, wet with rain. 'Come in, father. Come in quickly. Dry yourself by the fire,' cried the farmer, and his good wife gave the man a bowl of broth. They wrapped him in a blanket and he slept by the fire when everyone else had gone to bed.

Prince Attila had a small room leading off the kitchen and, in the middle of the night, he was woken by the sound of someone groaning. Going into the kitchen, he saw the old man lying there, clearly very ill. The voice of the fairy guardian said in the Prince's ear, 'The Apple of Life. Give him the Apple of Life.'

So Attila felt in his pocket and took out the precious apple. He gave the old man a bite and then another and soon the whole apple was eaten. The old beggar stopped groaning and a miraculous change came over him. His eyes became bright, his hair became black, his limbs became strong, and he stood up looking fifty years younger in ten minutes.

'Thank you, Prince Attila,' said he. 'In exchange for this kindness I will give you something, and here it is — the Ring of True Happiness, which I know you seek.'

Attila saw that he had in his hand a golden ring set with a strangely glowing opal stone. 'But how do you know who I am?' said Attila. 'Are you a wizard?'

'No, I was sent here by your fairy guardian to bring you this ring which I have had for many years. Now, because you have given me the Apple of Life, I shall be able pursue my secret quest for another fifty years.'

Next morning when the Prince woke, the traveller had gone. The farmer and his wife tried to make the young man stay longer, but he was eager to be on his way to the kingdom at the end of the world. So he gave them a gold piece, thanked them and rode away.

Attila let his horse carry him on and on until he came to a most desolate spot where there were mountains as far as the eye could see. They reached the safety of a great cave at nightfall and in the darkness of the cave, the fairy guardian appeared again to the Prince.

'You are not far from the end of the world,' said she. 'Tomorrow, you shall go through the pass and reach the palace of King Mendoza. I will help you to get the Mirror of Truth from him. Then you will be able to go back to your own country, Attila.' And then she vanished.

Next morning when the Prince woke, the sun was high in the sky. The horse carried him bravely through a narrow pass where huge rocks towered on both sides. In the distance he saw a gigantic castle perched on a mountain, right at the end of the world. There were a hundred turrets and on each turret shone a golden star. The road towards the castle was difficult, but Attila took his great horse carefully along the road and soon, there before them were the huge golden gates of the fortress castle of King Mendoza.

'What do you want?' asked the captain of the guard when the Prince knocked on the giant lion-head knocker.

'I have come to see King Mendoza,' said Attila boldly.

The vizier came to take him to the King, for His Majesty had seen Attila's arrival in the magic Mirror of Truth a few minutes before. King Mendoza was sitting on his carved ivory throne, but he didn't look happy. He said to Attila, 'I live in this golden castle and have a treasure house full of jewels, my stables are full of priceless horses, my dominions are the richest on earth, yet I do not know peace of mind.

Why is that?'

'Your Majesty,' said Attila, taking the Ring of True Happiness from his finger, 'try this and it will give you that which you have not got.'

No sooner did the ring touch King Mendoza's finger than the King felt happiness in every vein of his body and every hair of his head. He leapt from his throne, shouted with laughter and said, 'You shall have anything, anything in my kingdom that you need, for I am now the happiest man in the world.'

'May I have the Mirror of Truth?' asked Attila, and the King replied at once, 'Of course, with all my heart.'

So Attila stayed in the kingdom at the end of the world, and was feasted for seven days and seven nights. When at last he set off for home, the Mirror of Truth was in his saddle bag.

He travelled for many a day on the long journey back, until he was nearly home. Then, within a few miles of his palace, he saw a huge dragon in his path and in its jaws he saw that it had a girl. He rubbed his talisman three times and, rising up in the stirrups with drawn sword, he rode upon the creature shouting with all his might. With one mighty chop he cut off the dragon's head and it dropped dead. The girl whom he had saved told Attila that she was a charcoal burner's daughter and thanked him from the bottom of her heart.

'Come,' said the Prince. 'Get on the horse in front of me and I will take you home.' When he had looked at her for a few minutes, he decided that he had never seen anyone so beautiful, and he asked her to marry him. Her delighted smile gave him his answer.

Together, they rode majestically towards the palace. But all the houses and all the shops in the streets were closed fast, and no one came out to greet their prince as he came riding home. The gates of the palace were shut tight, and though the Prince banged with all his might, they remained closed.

So he pulled the Mirror of Truth out of his saddle bag and looked into it. He saw that everyone was in mortal fear of the great beast which he had just slain. So he waved his sword and shouted, 'Come out. Come out, everybody. Come out of your houses and your shops and open the palace. The dragon is dead. I have killed the dragon.'

At once, everyone came running out of their houses and their shops, cheering and glad to see their Prince back. They carried him into the palace on their shoulders. The charcoal burner's daughter was lost in the crowd, but the Prince soon found her and took her to his father.

The King was delighted to see him and complimented him on his beautiful bride. Then he asked, 'What about the Apple of Life and the Ring of True Happiness and the Mirror of Truth, for which I sent you to the end of world?'

So Attila told his father the whole story from beginning to end, sparing no detail, and gave him the Mirror of Truth.

'Then,' said the King, 'my dear son, you have brought me the best that a human being could possess, even though he be a King, for without truth what is happiness or life?'

The King, the Dog
and the Golden Bowl

ONCE UPON A TIME in Turkey, there lived a merchant called Hasan who was wealthy and generous, happy and fortunate. But one day disaster struck. His ships, bearing great loads of treasures from afar, were captured by pirates, and his warehouses, containing many valuables, burned down. Unable to face his friends, he sold his house and all his remaining belongings and set off in search of his fortune.

But his good luck had completely deserted him, for a thief stole his money while he was asleep in a caravanserai, and he found himself without a single coin to his name in a strange town. He went to the mosque keeper and asked for alms to see him on his way, feeling very ashamed of himself. He wondered how he was ever to hold up his head again, so he asked the mosque keeper what to do.

'My son,' said the old man, 'three days' march from here there is such-and-such a place. The King there is very charitable, and you may be able to put your case before him. Ask him for help of a more substantial nature than this which I am able to present to you out of our limited funds.' And he gave Hasan a handful of coins.

Hasan thanked him and set off, after buying a few dates to eat upon the journey. The way was rough and hard, so Hasan was tired and thirsty and his clothes were tattered by the time he arrived at the walled town. He could see that the shopkeepers were richly dressed and seemed contented.

He walked warily towards the palace where the old mosque keeper had told him that the King fed hundreds of people each night, but when he finally got there he was so ashamed of his rags that he hid behind a pillar, from where he could look upon the scene. There was a great concourse of people, young and old, being given food and money by the generous monarch, who sat upon a great throne in the middle of the lofty hall. From his hiding place behind the pillar, Hasan watched three large hounds being led to a place a few feet away from him. An attendant placed three bowls of the finest meat before the three dogs. The man then went away and Hasan found his eyes fixed upon the delicious meat which had been given to the animals. So great was his hunger that Hasan could joyfully have eaten even the leavings of dogs. At that moment, the dog nearest to him raised his eyes and looking at him in an almost human fashion, pushed its golden bowl towards Hasan. The famished man, unable to wait a moment longer, helped himself to one of the pieces of meat and pushed the bowl back to the dog. But with its paw, the animal again pushed it over to Hasan until he had eaten his fill.

Then the hound finished the meal and after it had licked its bowl clean, pushed it back towards Hasan. The man saw that it was offering him the bowl so he took it and hid the precious object under his tattered cloak. The dog seemed to nod its head in agreement. Hasan realised that if he sold the bowl and bought himself new clothes, he would at least have a chance of getting himself a suitable position. He patted the hound gratefully on the head and slipped away from the crowd.

He sold the bowl to a goldsmith and got such a good price that he was able to set himself up in business in a small way, instead of having to apply for work. Soon, by clever buying and selling, he had enough merchandise to take back to his native town of Istanbul, where his friends greeted him with much joy. His good luck having returned, Hasan became a successful trader and in time was once more as rich as he had ever been.

But the affair of the golden bowl weighed upon his conscience and he felt an urge to return to that town where he had been shown such kindness by the dog. He knew that unless he replaced the valuable object which he had stolen, he would have no peace of mind at all.

Within a few days a replica of the golden bowl was ready. Taking his best horse and clad in flowing robes with boots of the finest leather, Hasan set off on the journey. At last the city came in sight and once again he saw the old wall which was built around the town. But, riding through the gates, he saw with dismay that the glory of the palace was no more. It lay wide open to the sky, roofless and ruined, its beautiful pillars broken as if it had been destroyed by Mongol hordes. The wrecked houses were silent and empty, the shops, where rich and contented merchants had sat, were despoiled of their merchandise and there seemed to be no living thing in the whole place.

Sorrowfully, Hasan was mounting his horse to ride away when a great hound dashed out of the palace ruins, quickly followed by two others. Hasan recognised the fine dogs which had been brought to feed from the golden bowls when he was a beggar. Then an old man appeared wearing a rough woollen robe and leaning heavily upon a stick.

'Greetings, my son,' said the old man. 'What brings you to this place?'

'Once upon a time I came here in rags,' said Hasan, 'and was fortunate enough to be given meat from the bowl of this dog. When I left, I'm afraid I took the bowl because I needed it. I sold it and replenished my fortune and now I have come to repay my debt and return the bowl to the owner.'

'All those times have gone,' said the old man. 'The vanity and pomp that was once my court has vanished.'

Then Hasan saw that this was indeed that generous King whom he had seen feeding the poor and needy in the great palace long ago.

'Your Majesty,' said he, 'please take this golden bowl which I have brought.'

'No,' said the old King. 'I have no need of anything except that which remains here. My hounds catch game for my one daily meal. My gardener has remained with me to grow vegetables and roses. Together he and I and the hounds manage to enjoy our lives in peace. After my enemies destroyed everything and my people were taken away, I have lived here very simply.'

'But the bowl, the golden bowl, shall I not leave it for Your Majesty?' said Hasan.

'If a dog of mine thought fit to give away his bowl,' said the King, 'it is not for me to expect you to return it. I'm sure he has no need of it now. Go, return from whence you came. By the grace of Allah, we are sufficiently provided for at the present time, and I dare say everything will be all right for the rest of our lives.'

Bowing to the King, Hasan mounted his horse and rode away. He looked back to see the old man leaning on his stick, waving a last farewell, before he disappeared into the ruins with his hounds about him. In after days, Hasan, now old and grey in his home in Istanbul, often told the story, so that men should not forget the tale of the King, the dog and the golden bowl.

The Lady Who Came Out of a Cupboard

ONCE UPON A TIME there lived in Turkey a very rich merchant who had a son called Mustafa. For years, everything that the young man desired had always been given to him. One day he said to his father:

'I am now fully grown, father, and no longer want to live at home with you and my brothers and sisters. I would like a fine house of my own set in a beautiful garden. Furnish it with all the treasures you can find and I will be as happy as the day is long.'

So as you can see, he was very spoiled. The merchant duly prepared a beautiful house for Mustafa with everything that was needed to make it a luxurious home and the merchant's son went to live there. And every day, Mustafa's mother used to send him fine dishes cooked with her own hands for his meals.

One day Mustafa found a small nest in one of the bushes in his garden and took from it a tiny blue egg. Putting it away in his cupboard he then forgot all about it. But this was a magic egg which had been put in the nest by a fairy, and one night, while the merchant's son was sound asleep in his bed, the egg hatched and out came a beautiful lady.

Thereafter, every day, the beautiful lady in the cupboard used to come out and eat what was left of the dishes sent by Mustafa's mother before the servants came to take them away to the kitchen.

One day Mustafa came back into his room after having finished his midday meal and saw the beautiful lady helping herself from one of his dishes.

'Who are you?' he asked. 'And how did you get into my house?'

'I do not know who I am,' said the lady. 'I came from that cupboard there and I have never known any other home.'

'No longer shall you live in a cupboard, my dear,' said he. 'You shall be my guest and live in one of the largest and most beautiful rooms in this house.'

'Thank you,' said she. 'It certainly is a little cramped in the cupboard.'

So Mustafa sent a message to his mother to tell her that he had now met the girl he was going to marry and then his happiness in his new home would be complete. His mother soon arrived to inspect her son's intended bride and was delighted with Mustafa's choice; the wedding was celebrated without delay.

Mustafa gave his bride the name of Karagoz, meaning 'black eyes', and she lived happily with him for many years. In due course, two sons were born to Mustafa and his wife whom they named Oleg and Timorz.

When they were grown into fine young men and each had taken a wife, Karagoz fell gravely ill. She called for her sons, blessed them and their wives, and thus was the lady in the cupboard called to Allah.

Some time later, a fisherman brought a most beautiful fish to the house of Mustafa. It had bright green eyes and was covered from head to tail with gleaming silver scales. Never before had anyone seen such a beautiful fish. The fisherman said, 'If any man eats of this fish, when he cries, pearls will drop from his eyes and when he laughs, diamonds will fall from his lips.'

Mustafa at once bought the fish for a price of one thousand pieces of gold. Since the death of the Lady Karagoz, Mustafa's cooking was done by the wife of his son, Oleg, the elder boy.

'My dear,' said he to his favourite daughter-in-law, 'please cook this fish for me with your own hands and give it to me when it is done. I would like to have it for my evening meal.'

She agreed and took it away to the kitchen.

Now this daughter-in-law was a sweet and charming girl, but the wife of Timorz, the other son, was as different from her as chalk is from cheese. She was wicked at heart and cunning in every way. She had overheard the conversation between her father-in-law and the fisherman and she also heard Mustafa ask Oleg's wife to cook the fish for him. At once, she decided to steal the fish and give it to her own husband to eat so that it would be he who could drop pearls from his eyes and diamonds from his lips.

She sent for her old nurse, a wicked witch, and told her to put a spell on her father-in-law, her sister-in-law and her brother-in-law which would make them fall asleep forever so that she could steal the magic fish. However, as she was whispering to the old woman, a lazy servant who had been lying under the bed having a secret nap, over-heard, and crept out to tell his mistress, Oleg's wife.

Oleg's wife immediately told her husband and he

decided that they should leave the house for a while, going away in disguise to a forest. Just then, Timorz came in and asked his brother, 'Where are you going? My wife was looking for you a little while ago to give you a present for your birthday.'

Oleg told his brother all that had happened and how he had learned of his sister-in-law's plot to put them all to sleep forever by witchcraft. Oleg's wife, who was with child, was weeping and wailing but Timorz said to her, 'Do not cry, my sister. Let us all go away together. Come, we will eat the fish ourselves, and leave the wicked woman to her plotting.'

They all ate — enjoying the strange fish very much — then dressed quickly in simple clothes, and taking a box of jewels with them, slipped out into the night. There was only one horse in the stables, a huge white stallion, so the three leapt upon its back and galloped away.

They rode and they rode, on and on, until they were far, far away from their home. The moon rose and still they rode on. Presently the horse grew tired and slowed down at the edge of a large forest.

The three fugitives slipped to the ground and Timorz at once began to collect wood for a fire to keep the wild animals of the forest at bay. Oleg went on into the forest to see if he could find more wood and after a little while, he lost his way. He was looking around for a way to get back to his brother and his wife when, suddenly, there appeared before him a huge elephant. Its harness was colourfully painted and decked with jewels, and it trumpeted with all its might. On its back a great golden howdah, the seat set with precious gems. Very gently the animal picked up Oleg with its trunk and placed him upon the howdah. Slowly but surely, the elephant then made its way through the forest, taking the amazed Oleg towards a large city which gleamed as white as marble in the moonlight.

The gates opened as the elephant approached and a huge crowd gathered, even though it was the middle of the night. 'The elephant has brought us our new King!' cried the people and they all bowed down before him. The elephant knelt and a very great personage who was the Vizier of that kingdom came forward and welcomed him: 'Your Majesty,' he said by way of explanation, 'every year when our King dies, this elephant goes forth to bring us a new ruler. He and he alone is empowered to find our monarch.'

'But, but… how is it that every year you need a new King?' asked Oleg uneasily.

'What happens we do not know, but every twelve months to the day our ruler dies — be he young or old, timid or bold, handsome or ugly. Each time another one is chosen by this elephant and he is married to the queen and rules us as long as he is able. Alas, so far the queen has had fifteen husbands, and each one was found lifeless in the royal bedchamber twelve months after the marriage.'

Without further ado, Oleg was taken to meet the queen, who greeted him with joy. She was young and exquisitely beautiful, without any sign on her face of the suffering she must have undergone at the death of fifteen husbands.

'Come to the royal bedroom, my lord,' said she in a voice like a nightingale and led him to a silk-hung room. There servants undressed him, giving him a linen bedrobe to wear, and withdrew without turning their backs upon him. The queen had disappeared.

'So, I am a King now, am I?' said he to himself and lay down on the silken, jewel-sewn coverlet. Uneasily, he wondered what was going to happen next, so he half-closed his eyes and pretended to be asleep. In a few minutes he heard a faint rustling movement and he saw that the queen was gliding into the room. A ray of moon-light fell on her face and Oleg saw that she was very much changed although she was still wearing her royal robes. Her face was transformed as he watched and in a trice she had become a gigantic green snake.

He leapt up and caught the creature around the neck. Holding on to it, he reached for his dagger and cut off its head. At the very moment that the snake was killed, the beautiful young queen appeared again. The spell had been broken, the evil was gone and with it went all memories of the tragic events. All was well with the kingdom once more.

Thus, the young man forgot all about his own wife and his brother, and he settled down with the queen to rule the land from the great alabaster city as if he had never done anything else.

Meanwhile, at sunrise by the riverbank, Timorz looked anxiously for his brother but could see no sign of him. He returned to his sister-in-law and she saw from his face that something was wrong.

'A wild beast must have carried Oleg off into the forest, or maybe a crocodile has taken him in the river,' she said, and she bowed her head in grief.

'Well — I will go back to the river again. Perhaps he

will be there now,' said Timorz. So he left her under a tree with the casket of jewels and set off again, hoping against hope that his brother was alive. When he reached the river and saw that his brother had not come back that way, he began to weep, and the tears that fell from his eyes turned into pearls — because he had eaten of the magic fish.

Just then a boatman came past and saw a young man weeping with what looked like a pile of pearls beside him. 'Aha,' said he to himself. 'This looks interesting.' Stealthily, he came to the bank and, taking him unawares, he caught hold of Timorz, tied him up and put him in the bottom of his boat.

'Please let me go free,' said Timorz, dropping more pearls into the boat. 'My brother is lost and my sister-in-law is alone on the edge of the forest.'

'No! I'm going to take you home with me and you shall make my fortune, young man,' said the cruel boatman, and he sailed down the river to his home.

There in a dark room, the poor young man wept often at the fate which had befallen him and thus he added to the pile of pearls every day. The wicked boatman took the pearls daily to the market to sell, saying that he had found them in the river.

Meanwhile at the edge of the forest, Oleg's wife gave birth to a boy with a strange birthmark on his hand in the shape of a hoopoe. Although she was alone and frightened, as time went by she forgot her fear. She nursed her baby and sang to him as the sun began to climb into the heavens. Presently, she fell asleep.

Now there came to the edge of the jungle a man who

was the prefect of police in that part of the country. He had no children of his own and when he saw a poor woman in bedraggled clothes lying asleep beside the path with a baby in her arms, he decided to steal the child. Quietly, he took the sleeping boy from his mother's arms and slipped away into the forest.

The horror that Oleg's wife felt when she woke can scarcely be imagined: quite alone with her baby gone. She wandered through the forest all that day without food or water, weeping and calling until she was deep in the forest, completely lost.

An old man and his wife who lived in the middle of a clearing found her wandering, took her in and cared for her as if she had been born into their own family.

Two years passed.... The boatman who had imprisoned Timorz for so long fell ill and died. Timorz was able to escape, taking with him a large bag of pearls which he had found in the house. After selling the pearls in the town nearby, he travelled and travelled until he found himself back on the fringes of the forest, just where he had lost both his brother and his sister-in-law. There was no one to be seen so he sat down with his back to a tree, wondering which way he should go now.

It seemed but a few minutes before an old man with a young woman beside him came out of the forest. 'Here it was that I lost my husband and my brother-in-law on that night that my baby was born,' she was saying. And then her eyes fell upon Timorz and she ran to his arms. 'Dearest sister!' said he, 'how wonderful that I should have found you like this, more than two years since I was taken away.'

And he told his story from beginning to end.

She, in her turn, explained how she had come to be living with the old man and his wife, and that she had come with him that day to point out the place where they had all been together, two long years ago.

'Go now with your brother-in-law,' said the old man. 'Seek your husband and child, for I am sure they are alive. It is your duty to find them wherever they may be.' When they had made their farewells, he turned back into the forest.

On that very day, the absent-minded Oleg, who had now been King for more than two years, decided to go out hunting on his elephant, and he arrived at the very same spot not long afterwards. As soon as he saw the two figures sitting on the trunk of a fallen tree, his memory returned and he knew them. He made the elephant kneel and was happily reunited with his wife and his brother.

'Come with me to my kingdom, my dear ones,' he exclaimed and began to laugh with such delight that diamonds fell from his lips.

'But I cannot go with you until we have found our son,' cried his young wife. There and then, they all three decided to search for the child through the length and breadth of the land.

Travelling on the elephant in the jewelled howdah, they at last came to the house of the prefect of police where the baby boy was playing in the garden. The young mother had no sooner set eyes on the child than she knew he was her son because of the birthmark in the shape of a hoopoe on his right hand.

Oleg made the elephant kneel, and before the prefect of

police or his wife knew anything about it they had picked up the boy, put him into the howdah and the elephant bore them all away. After a long journey, the elephant brought all four back to the royal palace of white alabaster and its beautiful queen came out to receive them.

'Who are these people, my lord King?' she asked Oleg when she saw them descending from the elephant.

'It's a long tale,' said he. They all went into the palace and he told her the whole story from beginning to end. 'And,' he continued, 'this is my first wife. So though you are the queen, she shall be my favourite and you and she must both be as sisters to each other.'

Then the two women embraced one another and both promised to look after him as long as they should live. So they and the two brothers lived happily together in that far-away kingdom, dropping many diamonds from their lips as they laughed, but never again did any of them cry pearls from their eyes, for they were happy for the rest of their natural lives.

The Poor Bird-catcher
and the Talking Bird

ONCE UPON A TIME, not far from Istanbul, there lived a poor man. He used to catch birds by hanging nets in the trees of a forest, and then take them to be sold in a nearby town.

One day he caught a beautiful golden bird with a red beak, a yellow tail and a silver bell hanging from its right foot.

'Release me from this net, old man,' said the bird, 'for I am no ordinary bird and if you set me free I shall help you to make your fortune.'

Now this young man, whose name was Mehmet, could scarcely believe his ears when he heard the bird speaking in a human voice. At last he asked, 'How is it that a bird like you can speak and yet be so foolish as to get caught in my net?'

'Alas,' replied the bird, 'I did not look where I was going and I got my feet imprisoned like this. My mistress, who is the Princess, was hunting in the forest with her brothers and I was sitting happily on her wrist. Suddenly a hawk swooped down on me from the sky, and in fright, I flew from my mistress's wrist into the darkest part of the forest. The Princess will be desolated at my disappearance for she used to tell me all her secret thoughts and she taught me to talk so that I could be a companion for her.'

'Will you come and live in my little hut and talk to me?' asked Mehmet.

'Oh, no, no!' said the bird. 'You must take me back to my mistress at once. She will be missing me very much and will reward you with many pieces of gold when you return me safe and sound.'

'But how can I, a poor bird-catcher, find my way to the palace of so great a lady as your mistress?'

'Let me perch on your shoulder and I will tell you the way,' said the bird, 'but first give me some water to drink and some grain to eat, for I am faint from thirst and hunger.'

So the bird-catcher took the bird back to his little hut and gave it some water to drink. He put some grain on the palm of his hand so that it could sit in comfort on his wrist and feed. When the bird felt stronger it said:

'You must take me back to my mistress now. I cannot fly there because of the hawks in the sky and the palace is miles away.'

So Mehmet put on his tattered robe and his patched sandals and set off. The bird perched on his shoulder as he walked along and pointed out the way. At last, they came to a huge mountain and Mehmet went up a winding track until they reached a beautiful, red marble palace.

'Knock on the door and ask for the captain of the guard,' said the bird when they reached a huge brass studded door in the palace wall. Mehmet did so and the captain of the guard, who had black whiskers and beady black eyes, shouted at him, 'Who are you to dare to ask for me, you tattered rogue?'

'I have brought back the Princess's bird,' said Mehmet,

which made the captain of the guard open the great door leading to the courtyard of the palace.

'Oh you have, have you? Give me the bird and be off for you can't come any further,' said the captain.

'The Princess will give a large reward for my return,' twittered the bird ringing its tiny silver bell. 'You must let him pass, captain of the guard, or my mistress shall know about this.'

No sooner had the captain heard these words than his eyes grew round with greed. 'Then I shall claim the reward myself,' he shouted.

But the Princess Ninovar, leaning from her balcony, saw what was happening and she clapped her hands in delight. 'My darling golden bird has come back,' she cried and ran down into the courtyard with her slave girls all about her.

When the captain of the guard saw her, his face went very red. Then the Princess Ninovar took her pet back onto her wrist and asked Mehmet to tell her the whole story.

'You shall have as many pieces of gold as you can carry,' said the Princess Ninovar, 'for I would not lose my talking bird for all the world. And what do you do?' she continued, looking at him and seeing that he was a fine, strong young fellow and not minding at all that his robe was tattered and he had broken sandals.

'I am a bird-catcher, Your Highness,' said he, 'and I live in the forest. Every day, I put out my nets and when I catch enough birds I sell them in the town.'

'Why,' said the Princess, 'you shall stop being a bird-catcher from this very day, for you must come and look after the birds in the palace aviary.'

The Grand Vizier was summoned. He took Mehmet away and gave him a hundred pieces of gold, and a quantity of fine clothes befitting his new position. The Princess went to her brothers and told them that she would marry Mehmet and no other or remain alone until the end of her days. She was so determined that her brothers agreed and caused a great feast to be prepared in honour of their sister's wedding.

And so Ninovar and Mehmet were married and lived happily ever afterwards in a great palace overlooking the Bosphorus.

❧ TALES FROM PERSIA ❧

Princess Feroza
and the Horse Prince

ONCE UPON A TIME in the country of Iran, there lived a beautiful princess called Feroza, which means turquoise. She dwelt in a great castle on a high mountain and she was very lonely. She had lived in the castle ever since she could remember and she played upon the marble floor of the women's quarters where her mother, the Shah Banu, held court. Her father, the Shah-in-Shah or King of Kings, was far away, visiting the furthest part of his dominions, and she missed him. Her mother was so great a lady that she had no time to play with her daughter. She only liked visits from the queens of other countries and the choosing of new jewellery and discussions about new robes.

Her father, on the other hand, always played with Feroza and had taught her chess. But when the Shah-in-Shah was away there was no one with whom the princess could play chess, for all the courtiers were sure to let her win every game out of respect.

So one day the princess put on boys' clothes and a quilted coat and, taking her favourite horse Salem, she rode away to find her father.

She rode on and on until she reached the bank of a great river of white water. The current was so strong that she was afraid, but the brave Salem, who had been one of her father's war horses, plunged boldly in and took her to the other side. There on dry land stood a small and ugly *dev*, a monstrous creature. It had huge teeth as sharp as a crocodile's, and hair as thick and black as a bear's coat.

'Human being,' said the *dev*, 'do me a favour and you shall have anything your heart desires.'

'What is it you want?' said the princess boldly, for she didn't want to let the *dev* know she was frightened. She got down off her horse and stood bravely before the horrible creature.

'Take this message to my brother who lives in yonder castle,' the *dev* commanded, pointing to a towering castle on top of a distant hill, 'and he will grant you anything you ask for my sake.'

'Very well,' agreed the princess. 'Give me the message.'

'When you get to the fortress, tell my brother that I have turned the Shah-in-Shah into a pebble, which I have here in this purse, and I shall make myself the Shah of the whole of Iran in his stead. Be so good as to bid him to come to my enthronement, which will be held in the capital city of Isfahan in six days. The excellent fellow will then grant your wish. Now mount and go your way.'

The bewildered Feroza dumbly got into the saddle and rode to the mountain fortress of the second *dev*. How was she to save her father, who now lay in the first *dev's* purse, turned into a pebble? She tried to think of a plan but nothing would come. On went her brave steed, fleet as the wind, and soon they were at the gate of a castle, great and strong.

'Open, oh *dev*,' cried the princess, though her heart was

in her mouth. 'I have a message from your brother by the white river.'

Immediately the gate flew open and there was another *dev*, uglier and more wicked looking than the first.

'Enter, boy!' he roared. 'You shall taste of my hospitality. What message have you brought?'

'Your brother bids you to his enthronement in Isfahan in six days time as he has captured the Shah-in-Shah and plans to take his place.'

'Oh, excellent,' said the *dev*. 'Here, sit down on this divan and eat the meat from this bone. You look hungry. What do you ask as a favour?'

'I would like to be given a magic blade which will cut off the head of an enemy like lightning,' said the princess.

The *dev* laughed loud and long. 'Well spoken, boy, you shall have it,' he roared. 'You're a brave young fellow and deserve it.'

No sooner were the words out of his mouth than the princess felt a weight in her right hand and saw that she was holding a sword with a fine, damascened blade. She stuck it into its scabbard and leapt back into the saddle.

'See you at the coronation, then,' laughed the *dev* as Feroza rode away.

She galloped and galloped and finally arrived at the bank of the white river. There was the first *dev* sitting on an ox's skin. The princess towered above him on Salem's back.

'Well done, boy,' the *dev* roared. 'Have you had your reward?'

'Yes,' said the princess drawing her sword. And as the *dev* stepped forward to take a closer look, quick as lightning she cut off his head. She jumped from the saddle and searched his pockets, found the purse containing the pebble which was her poor father and rode back with it across the river once more.

By now it was night and Feroza sheltered in a cave, covered up with her quilted coat, with Salem standing at the entrance keeping watch over his mistress.

She slept till midnight and awoke to see a strange light at the end of the cave. A voice called, 'Awake, Princess, awake and listen to me, your *peri* guardian.'

The princess sprang to her feet and saw a beautiful fairy dressed in gleaming gold in the midst of a red fire. 'Give me the pebble, Princess,' said the *peri*. 'I will help you to restore your noble father to his human shape.'

The Princess was just about to hand over the stone when Salem, whinnying wildly, nuzzled her hand and the pebble fell to the ground. 'No, no, Princess,' the horse said in a loud voice. 'There is no *peri* — only a female *dev* who wants to get her hands on the Shah-in-Shah.'

As the horse spoke, the fire disappeared and the beautiful *peri* turned into a hideous woman, who also vanished with a sound like the hissing of snakes.

'But you spoke,' cried the Princess Feroza. 'Oh, help me to find the pebble. It fell here on the ground.'

'Here it is,' said the horse, catching up the pebble with its teeth.

The princess put it carefully into her pocket.

'How are you able to speak with the language of men though you are an animal?' asked the princess.

'I am an enchanted prince,' said the horse. 'I was put

under a spell on my eighteenth birthday because I spoke arrogantly to a sorcerer.' He tossed his mane with pride. 'But I am to be confined in this shape until such time as I am released by the love of a lady.'

'Oh, may it happen auspiciously,' said the princess, blushing. 'But now, let me mount you, good horse, and let us go to the wise woman of Isfahan so that we can find a way to turn my dear father back into the Shah-in-Shah.'

The princess sprang into the saddle once more and the horse sped with her across the land until at last they arrived at Isfahan. In a tall, shuttered house lived the wise woman of Isfahan. Her hair was white, her nose was curved like a parrot's beak and her green velvet dress was embroidered with the pink roses of Shiraz.

When at last the princess was in her study, the old woman heard the whole story without speaking. Then she said, 'I knew that you were coming for I looked in my magic mirror not one hour since. Yes, I have a special powder for turning the beloved Shah-in-Shah back into his own form. I must throw it upon the brazier.'

Tired and dirty, the astonished princess watched in amazement while the witch performed her magic. First the pebble was laid on the floor and the magic sign of King Suleiman was drawn around it. Then a pinch of the enchanted powder was tossed onto the burning coals. A few murmured words and the fire glowed red, then blue. Soon, to her great joy, the princess saw her father standing before her. The witch dropped to her knees but the Shah-in-Shah raised her to her feet.

'You shall have your mouth filled with jewels many

times for this, good mother,' declared the monarch.

The old dame babbled with delight.

The princess and her father returned to the palace and the brave horse neighed with pleasure when the princess kissed his moon-white ears and mane.

'I love you, dear horse-prince,' she murmured.

No sooner were the words out of her mouth than the horse disappeared, and there before her stood a tall handsome prince as fine as any in the world. And so they were married and there were seven days and seven nights of rejoicing in every town in Iran.

The Weaver and the Dev

ONCE UPON A TIME, long, long ago, there lived in old Nishapur a poor weaver called Abdul Latif whose wife, Fatima, was always saying to him, 'If only you had two heads and two pairs of hands, Abdul Latif, we'd have much more cloth and much more money to spend.'

One night, working away alone at his loom, Abdul Latif found a small *dev* entangled in his skeins of wool.

'Please help me to get out of this muddle, and I will grant you anything you ask,' said the *dev*.

The weaver helped the *dev* to escape from the skein and in return the *dev* said, 'Ask anything and I shall grant it to you.'

'My wife, Fatima, thinks I should have two heads and two pairs of hands,' said the weaver. 'Could you do this for me?'

'Granted,' said the *dev*, 'if that is what you want.'

Abdul Latif looked in the mirror and saw that he had two heads and two pairs of hands. He ran round the town crying, 'Look, look, see what has happened!' And the people all came out of their houses crying, 'A *dev*, a *dev*!' thinking he was a demon. They struck him with sticks and stones and drove him out of the town and he was never seen again.

So if you are ever given the chance of having a single wish granted, be very careful how you choose.

The Water-Carrier
and the Three Walnuts

*I*N A FAR AWAY PART of Persia, there lived a poor water-carrier and his wife. Every day they lamented the fact that they had no children, and when his day's work was finished the water-carrier would go and sit under a walnut tree. There he would dream that he had three strong sons who would keep them in their old age.

One evening he said, 'Oh walnut tree, if my wife and I had three sons to provide for our declining years, we would be the happiest people in the whole world.'

Now the tree beneath which he sat was a magical tree, bewitched by Suleiman himself; and when he had finished speaking, three walnuts fell beside him. They broke open and in each was a perfectly formed little boy. Each one called as he emerged, 'Here I am father, name me.'

So the water-carrier named them Mubarak, Masood, and Rashid. He took them home to his wife, full of joy. The boys grew up very fast — very soon they were taller and stronger than their parents. The water-carrier said, 'Sons, you should go out into the world now and earn enough money to keep your mother and me in comfort for the rest of our days.'

So they set out, taking with them an enchanted goat-skin of water and enough bread to last them a week. They walked on and on until, at the end of seven days they came to a great city. All the people were in mourning and all the women were crying. 'What is the matter in this city? Why is everyone so sad?' asked Mubarak.

'Our King's three daughters have been stolen and we are in mourning for them, for the King is good and noble and the princesses were the loveliest in all the land,' said an old woman snuffling into her veil.

Mubarak, Masood, and Rashid went to the palace and asked to see the Grand Vizier. 'Tell His Excellency we will find the princesses,' said they.

'What? How dare you three impecunious boys come here and ask to see our Grand Vizier,' shouted the captain of the guards. 'Be off with you or we shall cut your heads from your shoulders.'

At that moment the King came past on his way from the mosque, it being Friday, and heard the three young men speaking. He held up his hand and asked them to address their questions to him.

'Your Majesty,' said Mubarak, 'my brothers and I would like to help to get the three princesses back, for we have heard that they have been stolen. If you will tell us all about it, we shall go and rescue them.'

The King was astonished that three simple lads like these could come and speak so openly to him and he liked them at once.

'My soldiers have looked everywhere and my people are all in mourning, as you can see. If you can find my daughters, anything you ask shall be yours,' he said. 'Blessings be upon you. May you find them soon.'

The three brothers were taken to the royal kitchens and

given provisions enough for a week. Then they set out to look for the three princesses.

When they came to a crossroads they sat down and began to discuss their plans.

'Let us make our camp here,' said Masood. 'On the first day, one of us will go out and look westward and one of us eastward. The third will stay here and cook the food and rest. Then, on the second day, the others will go south and north while the third stays to cook and guard the camp.'

This they agreed and it was so for a week, but they found no sign of the King's daughters and in the four corners of the land nobody had any news which would help the brothers to find them. They were sitting round the fire, when a wizened old man walked into the firelight.

'Good evening, father,' said they together. 'Come and join us and warm yourself.'

'What are you cooking?' asked the old man, peering into the pot.

'This is a stew made from the last of our provisions,' said Masood, 'and now we shall have to go back to the King and tell him that we have failed to find his daughters.'

'Give me a plateful of your food and I will tell you what to do,' said the old man.

So they piled his plate until he had eaten nearly all there was, because they did not like to be impolite to a guest. When he had eaten his fill and was wiping his fingers on his beard, the old man said, 'My sons, I know where the King's daughters are hidden. If you will come with me, I will show you.'

He bade Masood take a burning stick from the fire to

light their way. So they left all their belongings and followed him into the darkness. He led them to a cave not far away. No sooner had they gone into the cave than they heard a laugh behind them and the voice of the old man said, 'Ha, ha, ha! Now I have you all in here — three young men and three princesses — and I shall fatten you all up until I am ready to eat you.'

A door had closed over the opening. The three brothers looked around them and in the light of the flare which Masood was holding, they saw the figures of three girls huddled in a corner of the cave.

'Have no fear, Princesses, we have come to save you,' said Masood. 'My brothers and I have been sent by your father, the King, to look for you.'

'But we are all prisoners,' cried the eldest princess. 'Our hands and feet are bound and we are faint from being held captive in this dreadful cave.'

No sooner had she finished speaking than there was a laugh from outside the cave and their captor said, 'No need to tell these silly young men all about it, my dear. They are prisoners just like you,' and they heard the old man cackling as he scampered away.

Masood spoke again, 'Listen Princesses, my brothers and I are no ordinary men for we were born of a magic walnut tree. We are possessed of the power to escape from any place where we may be held by virtue of our extraordinary strength. Watch…'

And as the girls watched in amazement, the three brothers pushed at the great cave door with all their might — and it opened. Then Mubarak untied the hands and feet of the three princesses and they all stole out of the cave and went back to the camp where the three brothers had prepared their meal. There was just enough left in the pot for all of them to have a little. As it was a bright, moonlit night they decided to start their journey back to the palace before the old man discovered that they had escaped.

By dawn next day, the three brothers and the three princesses were within sight of an oasis. When they looked back, they saw a very small cloud in the distance.

'Brothers, cover the princesses with our cloaks, for I do not like the look of that dust-cloud,' said Mubarak, but almost as he spoke, the old man appeared in their midst riding a racing camel, which was fast as the wind.

'Stop,' cried the old man, 'you are my prisoners, and I shall cast a spell upon you. Turn into pure gold, all of you!'

Now the princesses, being mortal, turned into golden statues and fell forward onto the ground, but the three brothers, who had been born of the magical walnut tree, each said a magic word and kept their own shape. The old man screamed with rage and lashed out at them in anger. But the three brothers shouted together:

'In the name of Suleiman, son of David, upon whom be peace, disappear!' and the old man and his camel vanished into thin air.

Then they went to the princesses who had been turned into pure gold and sprinkled over them a little water from the enchanted goat-skin, and the girls became human again.

The sun grew hotter and hotter and their feet sank into the sand so they could hardly walk. When finally they reached the oasis, Mubarak said, 'We'd better rest here for we cannot resist the heat of the sun, even with the power invested in us by Suleiman, son of David, upon whom be peace, whose slaves we are.'

The princesses sank down gratefully on the ground and drank, and bathed their feet, till the sun grew less hot.

Now a band of robbers came riding to that oasis to water their camels; when they saw the six travellers they became very curious.

'Where are you from, strangers, and whither are you bound?' they asked suspiciously.

'We are from such-and-such a place, brother, and are going to such-and-such a place,' said Masood, Mubarak and Rashid.

This terse reply enraged the bandits and they decided to attack the travellers as soon as night fell. But just as they were about to do so, the three brothers said with one voice, 'Fly away, evil ones, right into the sky.' A great wind rose and blew the bandits and their camels right up into the sky and out of sight and for all I know, they are still whirling about up there to this very day.

As soon as dawn came, the three brothers roused the princesses from their sleep and said a magic word, whereupon a camel with six humps appeared out of nowhere. The three princesses jumped up and each sat on a hump, as did the three brothers, and the great camel galloped off with them to the palace.

When they arrived at the gate, the captain of the guard and his soldiers ran out and helped the three princesses to the ground. The brothers jumped to earth and the six-humped camel vanished leaving the townspeople rubbing their eyes in astonishment. Weary and dusty, the princesses were taken to the harem to be bathed, dressed and perfumed. As soon as the King heard the news of his daughters' return the three brothers were given every honour and the King thanked them from the bottom of his heart.

That night there was a feast, the like of which the city had never seen before, and Mubarak, Masood and Rashid sat in places of honour near the King himself.

'Young man,' said the King to the nearest of the three, 'in the presence of all in this assembly I ask you and your brothers to name anything you desire. For bringing back my dear daughters when nobody else could find them, it shall be yours.'

'Noble King,' said Masood, 'I want nothing.'

'Noble King,' said Mubarak, 'I want nothing.'

'Noble King,' said Rashid, 'I want nothing.'

'Well said!' cried the King. 'Cause their mouths to be filled with gold and jewels.'

All the courtiers cheered as the treasurer was summoned and the three brothers had their mouths filled with gold and gems of great price.

Now the three princesses wanted to marry the three young men who had saved them and the King agreed. However Mubarak, Masood and Rashid wanted to get back to the old water-carrier and his wife who had brought them up, to give them the gold and the jewels.

'This will keep them in plenty for the rest of their days,' they said to each other, for they were very fond of the old couple. So while the three princesses were getting ready to have a triple wedding, the young men left in a hurry, sending to each princess a golden walnut with this message inside:

'A Princess cannot marry me
For I was born of a walnut tree.'

Mubarak, Masood and Rashid recounted the full story of their adventures to the old water-carrier and his wife, and presented them with the treasure. Then the three said goodbye to their foster parents, because they felt the urge to travel once more. And for all I know they are travelling yet, for the old water-carrier and his wife never saw them again.

Rustam and the Iron Fortress

ONCE UPON A TIME there lived in old Iran a famous hero named Rustam. He had been born in the days of the fabled Simurg, a bird with magical powers in every feather. She had brought up Rustam from earliest childhood and when he left her she gave him a feather saying,

'If at any time you need me, drop this feather into the fire and I will come to you, and save you from any disaster, whatever it may be.'

So Rustam went out into the world. He hunted lions and tigers, fought with giants and *devs* and had a magic lion-skin hat which made him invisible when he pulled it over his head.

Now Rustam had an enemy, the evil Balman, who one day boasted to the court that he would defeat the mighty Rustam and bring him back in chains. He set off in pursuit of Rustam and when he found him, the two men fought and fought until they could fight no more, but lay gasping side by side upon the ground.

'Give yourself up. Be my slave,' said the wicked Balman.

'Never!' said Rustam, and with the last of his strength he rose, and went off leaving his enemy on the ground. Balman went back to the court and everyone asked him, 'Ha ha, what happened that you couldn't bring the mighty Rustam, hero of Iran, back in chains as you said you would?'

Then Balman's face was blackened; he was ashamed and he vowed in his heart that he would somehow trick Rustam into coming to him, and he would slay him as he slew wild beasts. So he built a gigantic castle, a fortress in the hills, and covered the outer walls with iron plates. It was the strongest fortress that there had ever been in the whole world, and he posted heavily-armed men all along the top of its walls. A wise man came forward prophesying that he would win if he fought Rustam. So he sent a message to Rustam that he wished to meet him there.

When Rustam, mounted on Roch, the horse which had taken him through many tournaments, galloped up to the gate of the fortress, Balman looked out with a big smile on his face. 'Welcome to my home, Rustam,' he cried. 'Enter my fortress so that we can fight. We shall soon see who is the mightest hero in all Iran.'

He opened the gate and sent out two terrible *afreets* of venomous aspect, called Yarapush and Quepush, who attacked Rustam as he came trotting in. With his gigantic club, Rustam, sent one of the *afreets* reeling away, while Roch lashed out with his hind legs and sent the other *afreet* flying. The two *afreets* were flung to the ground like sacks of beans and Rustam put on his lion-skin cap, which rendered him invisible in a trice.

When Rustam entered the second courtyard of the iron fortress, Balman could only see the horse and wondered how it was that Rustam had vanished. He cried, 'Search for Rustam in every nook and cranny of the fortress, for he has hidden himself somewhere. A thousand gold pieces for whoever finds him!'

All the soldiers and the *afreets* ran hither and thither but not one hair of Rustam's head could they see. Leaving his horse tethered at the gate, Rustam slipped from the saddle and crept silently to the very heart of the great iron fortress. He was going to fight the loathsome Balman, but only when he was ready. He looked into one room after another, seeing a roomful of jewels, then a roomful of barrels of gunpowder, and another filled with lances, shields and spears. Then he found a door with a large key in the lock; turning the key he found a beautiful girl in the room, tied by her hair to a hook on the wall.

He took off his cap of invisibility and said, 'Lady, from your appearance you must be a King's daughter. Let me help you.'

He released her hair from the hook and she was over-joyed. 'I am Manaz and I am most grateful to you,' she told him. 'I am a princess indeed, though how long I have been here, tied by my hair in this vile place, I do not know.'

'Come with me, then,' said Rustam, 'and I will see that you arrive safely back in your father's dominions. But first I must slay my enemy, for he has invited me here in order to slay me, so that he may become the hero of the whole of Iran.'

'Why then, good sir, you must be Rustam,' said she. 'Oh, yes, I beg you! Take me back to my father's country of Turkistan yourself — then I know that I shall arrive safely.'

'Put this cap of lion skin upon your head,' said Rustam, handing it to her, 'and follow me closely. I am now going to find Balman because we must fight. If anything should happen to me, burn this feather and ask my enchantress and protectress, the Simurg, to help you. She will transport you to your father's kingdom in her claws, as she used to take me.'

'Oh no, do not talk of anything happening to you,' whispered the Princess. She put on the cap, and with the feather in one hand, she crept behind Rustam along the dark passage to the main courtyard.

Suddenly a group of soldiers appeared and seized Rustam, recognising him by his lion-skin coat. He was overpowered by the *afreets*, Yapush and Quepush, and dragged before Balman, who was sitting on his black iron throne.

'So, great Rustam, there you are!' mocked Balman. 'Come, let us fight one another and soon I shall be the greatest man in all Iran.'

So they fought and fought, when the sun was overhead and when the moon rose and when the stars shone in the sky. The soldiers and the *afreets* stood in a circle cheering their master on, but there was no one to cheer for Rustam except Manaz, and she dared not make a sound for fear of being discovered. But when she saw that Rustam, weak from many wounds was lying on the ground unable to rise, she threw the Simurg's feather into the fire which was burning within a great brazier in the courtyard. Instantly, with a rush of wings, the great bird was overhead.

Just as Balman was about to strike Rustam's head from his shoulders the Simurg blew out every torch in the fortress. 'Who dares to attack Rustam?' cried the Simurg with the voice of thunder. 'He is under my protection! By Suleiman, upon whom be peace, turn to stone, all ye evil ones!' And she fanned Rustam with her wing feathers so that he revived at once.

There was not a sound in the iron fortress — all had been turned to stone. Rustam helped Princess Manaz into the saddle of his faithful horse. 'Go, ride ye in peace to Turkistan,' said the Simurg kindly, and gave Rustam another feather before she flew away on mighty wings, high into the night sky.

Out through the fort's gateway they rode, the horse's hooves clip-clopping on the stones. The princess sang to Rustam as they travelled all the long way to Turkistan. When they arrived there, the King of Turkistan gave a feast lasting seven days and seven nights in honour of Rustam. When he left, the King ordered his mouth to be filled with gold.

And that was but one of the many adventures of Rustam, the Alexander, the Hercules of old Iran.

The Shah's Ring

ONCE UPON A TIME there was a Shah who went walking through the streets of his capital disguised as a dervish, a wanderer, to see the state of the city's affairs. He had on an old patched cloak and broken sandals so that none knew him to be the Shah. But he had forgotten to take off a very fine and exceedingly rare ruby ring and as he walked, it shone in the sunshine like a drop of blood. A thief chanced to be coming behind the Shah and saw it.

He thought to himself, 'Ha ha, that is a ring that I shall own before the night comes,' and he began to follow the Shah through the narrow markets, never letting him out of his sight.

In that city there were many fountains, with golden fish swimming about in marble basins. It was near the Grand Mosque, beside one of these tinkling fountains of clear, cool water, that the Shah stopped when the heat of the afternoon was at its worst, to dip his hand in the water. As he did so, the ring slipped off without his noticing, but the thief was watching and when the Shah moved away, he plunged his hands into the water to see if he could find it. But the ring was nowhere to be found, which was not surprising as a fish had swallowed it.

Cursing his bad luck, the thief gave up the search and went off to rob a man who was passing, wearing a very fine emerald on a gold chain.

When the Shah got back to his palace he realised he had lost his ring, but being a philosopher, he said to himself, 'It is the will of Allah that my ring has gone. Perhaps this is a way of showing me that I have too many possessions. Mysterious and wonderful are the ways of Allah.' And he went to bathe and change before visiting the Queen, Shah Banu.

Now Queen Shah Banu had a slave girl called Zuhra who was as brown as a date, for she was from Africa. Zuhra was very fond of playing with the golden carp in the fountain in the courtyard of the harem and that day she took one of the fish out of the water to stroke its golden scales. Just as she was about to drop it back into the fountain, Queen Shah Banu's pet Persian cat jumped up and caught it. The cat killed the fish and then ran away and lay at its mistress's feet purring and washing its fur. Zuhra was terrified, for there were always twelve fish in the fountain in the harem. Each day, Queen Shah Banu counted them herself.

What was to be done? Queen Shah Banu had a very bad temper and had warned Zuhra several times not to take the fish out of the water in case they should die. So Zuhra veiled herself completely, picked up a small bowl and went to the Chief Eunuch.

'Let me pass, Aga, for I have to go and get some curd for my mistress,' she said, for none could leave or enter the harem without the permission of the Chief Eunuch. 'Here is the bowl in which I am to bring it, and quickly or the Queen Shah Banu will have me beaten.'

'All right, girl, hurry on then, and be sure you are back

by dark or you will find the gate locked and barred,' cried the eunuch.

Running as fast as her legs could carry her, Zuhra came to the fountain where swam the fish which had swallowed the Shah's ring. Quick as a flash she slipped one of the fish into the bowl she carried, with a little water to keep it alive. When she got back to the harem it was nearly dark and the Chief Eunuch was looking out for her.

'Hurry inside, my girl. I must lock the door,' he said crossly, peering at her with his large, short-sighted eyes.

Zuhra, holding her hand over the bowl to hide the fish from his gaze, tiptoed past him into the harem and the great door clanged shut. With a sigh of relief, she dropped the fish into the Queen Shah Banu's fountain. There were again twelve fish swimming about in the shimmering water. And strange as it may seem, this fish which Zuhra had brought was the very same one which had swallowed the Shah's ring.

When he had bathed and changed into fresh clothes, the Shah came to the harem and enjoyed the company of his wife and three daughters as they plied him with sweetmeats and sherbet.

'Oh most auspicious lord,' said the Queen Shah Banu, 'where is the beautiful ruby ring, the finest in all Persia, which my father sent as a seal of our marriage pact twenty years ago.'

'Oh peace, wife,' answered the Shah. 'I lost it today. I do not know where, but it was while I wandered through the streets disguised as a dervish to see for myself the state of affairs. If Allah wills that I should lose it, who am I to go against the Divine Will? Perhaps it is to teach me the futility of having too many worldly possessions.'

'Why, my Lord,' cried the Queen Shah Banu. 'Amassing treasure for its own sake is unworthy, but that is a jewel which I would dearly love to see back on your finger. Let me summon my sooth-sayer and ask her to find out where the ring may have gone.'

The Shah tried to dissuade her but the lady persisted and in the end, as he saw there would be no peace until she had had her way, he relented. Then the Queen said to Zuhra, 'Go, bring the sooth-sayer here and get her quickly for I must get to the bottom of this matter tonight.'

So Zuhra hurried away to find the old woman who sat mumbling in her room, her tattered robe down to her ankles and her snake-like white locks capped with a crown of coins. When she could make the sooth-sayer listen to her, Zuhra said, 'Good mother, come quickly to the harem. My mistress, Queen Shah Banu, wants you to find the ruby ring which my lord, the Shah, lost today in the city.'

The old sooth-sayer came to the harem where she bowed low before the Shah and kissed Queen Shah Banu's hand. Then she arranged her mystic charms on a tray, muttering to herself.

'What say you, sooth-sayer?' asked Queen Shah Banu. 'Where lies the ruby ring which my Lord lost today?'

And the sooth-sayer answered, 'I can see... I can see it is somewhere... somewhere dark.' She peered at her charms, then closed her eyes.

'Somewhere dark?' Queen Shah Banu repeated while the Shah looked on in amusement. 'Whatever do you mean?'

'Yes, yes… somewhere dark. It is not very far from this spot. It is… it is… at this moment in the harem.'

'In the harem? Why, you must be out of your wits,' cried Queen Shah Banu. 'It was in the streets of the city that the Shah lost the ring.'

'Yes, most gracious Lady, but it is now in the harem, and was brought here soon after it was lost.'

'Somewhere dark,' mused the Shah. 'Is it in a cupboard?'

'No my Lord. It is not.'

'Then is it in a bag?'

'No, my Lord. It is not.'

'Is it under the floor?'

'No, most Auspicious One, it is not, but it is surrounded by water. And now, ah ha, I have it,' the sooth-sayer gave a cackle of triumph. 'It is in a fish.'

'In a fish, by my faith,' shouted the Shah. 'This is the biggest jest I have ever heard.'

'Explain more fully,' said Queen Shah Banu. 'How did it get into a fish in the first place?'

After a pause, the sooth-sayer intoned, 'My lord's ring fell from his hand into a fountain near the Grand Mosque. A fish swallowed it and the slave girl, Zuhra, brought the fish here to replace the one the cat ate.'

With this, the old woman finished and closed her eyes as if in sleep.

'Zuhra,' shrieked Queen Shah Banu, 'Come here at once! How did the cat eat one of my fish? Were you playing with them again? What have you been doing? Explain yourself this instant!'

Then Zuhra threw herself at the Shah's feet and begged

for his protection from the wrath of his lady. Trembling, she kissed the hem of Queen Shah Banu's robe and told what had happened from beginning to end.

'And it was the fish with the blue fins which I picked out of the marble basin outside the Great Mosque,' she sobbed. 'I can show you it if you will have mercy upon me, Great Ones.'

The Shah smiled and looked at Queen Shah Banu. 'I think we can allow this to pass on just this one occasion,' said he. Then to the girl he said, 'Bring the fish and let us see if the ring is indeed inside.'

No sooner said than done. And as Zuhra held the golden carp with blue fins in her hands, it coughed up the ring onto the floor.

With a cry of joy, Queen Shah Banu picked up the gleaming ruby and put it back onto the Shah's finger. 'Since Zuhra has been the means of bringing the fish here, I will allow her action to go unpunished,' she said.

The Shah caused the sooth-sayer's mouth to be filled with gold so that she went away rejoicing. And Zuhra never touched Queen Shah Banu's fish again for all the rest of her days.

❧ AMERINDIAN TALES ❧

The Girl of the Great Mountain

This is a story that the Shoshoni storymakers tell and which comes to us from the diary of a missionary doctor who worked with them for years. This must be the American-Indian version of the Adam and Eve story.

ONCE THERE WAS A TIME when there was only the earth and the sky and flowers, birds, fruits, nuts and animals, but no people: only one girl who lived alone on the great mountain. And there was harmony about her in those days when the world began. The great mountain was beautiful, its top covered with snow. Every morning when the girl woke, she came out of the cave where she had spent the night and ran down the mountain and gathered fruits for her meal. Then she looked for scented, golden flowers to put in her hair. She played with the birds as they settled on her hand while she was picking fruit, and she played with the fish as they came to her when she washed herself in the great lake at the foot of the mountain. And her hair was long and black and shining, like the wings of night.

Now the girl had never seen anything like herself. One morning when she came down the mountain and was bathing in the water of the lake, she felt uneasy and looked towards the western shore of the lake. There she saw something standing and watching her. It was a tall animal with hair on its face and some sort of fur and leather clothing fastened around its body and it was quite strange to her. It walked upright as she did, and had two arms and two legs.

She came out of the water, covered by her long black hair which hung round her like a cloak, and said, 'What are you and where do you come from?'

The other being answered, 'I am a man and I will be your friend. We will go about the world together for it is beautiful, and find out what it is for, and how far it is from one mountain to another, and from one lake to another. I think we will have much happiness together.'

He smiled at her and held out his hand. She laughed and that was the first time that she had ever laughed so happily.

So the girl of the great mountain took his hand and walked with the man through the newly made world. They had great happiness. She called him the Man of the Great Mountain, for they always returned there every time they wanted to be at harmony with the earth and the water and the sky. They made many discoveries together: how to swim in the lake instead of just bathing in it, how to catch fish and dry them in the sun, and how to make jewellery for the girl from shells and stones — which the first man learned to drill with small holes and to hang on long, thin pieces of dried vine.

Now one day when they had been sitting in the shadows of the towering trees which shaded them from the heat of the sun, the man said to the girl, 'I think I will go alone today and get you something to wear, for I have made this tunic from a hide for myself, and I know you will be happy to have one. Also, you will be needing it soon.'

So she said goodbye to him and he went away with his

flint knife in his hand He was gone a long time. After many days away, he came back at last and threw down a beautiful fur in front of her saying, 'This is your robe. Look, we will tie it around you with creepers and fasten your hair back with flowers and you will be the most beautiful being in the whole, newly-made world.'

'But what is it?' asked the girl, 'And where did you get it?'

'I tracked it and killed it,' said the man, 'and I ate the meat and buried the rest for when we may need it again. I dried the skin and here it is for you to wear. Soon the snow will come and you will need it.'

'But you have killed one of the animals!' cried the girl. 'Why have you done that? Were they not put in the world by the Great Spirit just as we were, to live and enjoy life and have nothing but pleasure and harmony here? The animals are all my friends and you have killed one.'

'There is not only pleasure in the world,' said the man. 'There is joy, yes, and harmony, but there is also killing and hardship. I have travelled much further in the world than you have, and I have had to kill many animals to live and to clothe myself, just as animals also kill to live.'

'I cannot agree with you,' said the girl. 'I have only known pleasure and happiness in all my time here in the world. There are only sunny days here, only warmth and pleasure.' She ran away from him into the woods, and however hard he tried, he could not catch her.

He gave up trying to find her and went to a clearing and lit himself a fire and roasted a small animal. Then he lay down beside the fire to eat it, and eventually he went to sleep wrapped in the great fur robe he had brought for the girl. He did not worry, for this was the first argument they had ever had and he knew he was in the right and could afford to be patient. For the Great Spirit had told him that the winter was coming and that the girl of the great mountain should no longer be left to live in the cave, or she would freeze to death without a warm robe to wrap herself in. But he waited and slept peacefully until she had learned her lesson.

Now that night the wind blew so fiercely that nearly all the remaining leaves were carried away from the trees. The night grew colder and colder, making the stars shine brighter. The girl lay in her cave on the great mountain and shivered. Before morning, the snow came silently, thick and fast so that it almost blocked up the entrance to the cave. When the girl awoke she rubbed her eyes, knowing it must be day because she had slept the usual time. But she panicked because she could not see the entrance to the cave.

She made her way to the place where she knew the cave mouth must be and there she saw a little daylight. With her hands, she clawed away the ice and snow, making a larger opening. Outside, the mountain was silent and covered with deep snow. How was she going to survive if this happened again? For hours she sat blowing on her fingers and scraping away at the snow, until she had made an opening big enough for her to get out and make her way to the place where she knew the man would be waiting.

How she knew, we cannot guess. What told her, we have ourselves long ago denied that we can hear, but she was the first woman and she knew how to find the first man. So when they were reunited and she had warmed herself beside his fire, and eaten of his meat, she asked in a small voice, 'Can I have my robe now so that I can be warm in this winter weather and warmer than I was in my cave?'

'Then,' said the man, 'will you agree with me in what I tell you from now on, and cook for me the meat I will kill, and travel with me over this newly-made world? For we have so much to see and to do before the world becomes old and drops back into the sea.'

'Well,' said the first woman, the girl of the great mountain, 'I will try to agree with you in everything that you say and do. I promise to cook your meat for you and travel with you over this newly-made world until it drops back into the sea. But what will you give me for this promise? A promise for a promise until the end of the world.'

And the first man answered, 'I will always give you furs to wear and build you a lodge to live in that will be cosy and warmer than your cave; and I will make holes in shells so you can wear them around your neck. And I will look after you for all the days of your life.'

As it was with our first father and mother, so it is with us. For do men not still build the lodges and give their wives the furs of animals? And so it must be until the end of time, when the world drops back into the sea.

Bearwoman and the Little Navajo

*S*OON AFTER THE EARTH was made there lived a little Navajo boy. He spent all his time talking to the animals which were his friends, for there were not many boys of his own age with whom he could play.

He would go to a certain place where there were many small animals which he tamed with pieces of food, and until the cold time came, the whole year passed in great happiness for him.

He had no father or mother for they had both died together soon after he was born, when the great hunger came, and his grandmother had brought him up. Often he used to sit very quietly playing with his pets, thinking how nice it would be if he had a mother like other boys or a father who was a hunter. In his imagination, the great cliffs were fortresses manned by people who were fabulously wild and brave. They would invite him into their strongholds and teach him all their lore, how to make bows and arrows and silver jewellery and how to paint pictures of animals and birds that would have magic in them beyond all telling.

He imagined that the thunder which he often heard far up in the sky was the roaring of some colossal animal — what, he could not guess. But he thought it must have at least three heads and six eyes like burning coals. He wished that he could paint such a creature.

There were caves at the foot of some of the cliffs.

Sometimes, he took a burning brand right inside one of them, in order to look at the wonderful paintings on the walls. There were pictures which were so clear in some parts that for a moment he really thought he was seeing some great monster there. And others were so faint that he wanted to mix colours from the clays and paint them all over again with his fingers.

One night he went to this cave with a torch of burning wood, just to be alone, and to think about his life. So far it had been a happy one, with not much to do but wait upon his grandfather and help his grandmother in small chores like fetching wood. But now he felt a strange longing to be alone and crept out to be there while everyone else was asleep.

The stars were very bright as he turned his face upwards, sitting at the entrance to his favourite cave. There was no moon as yet and he threw another piece of wood on the fire to keep away the coyotes, which howled their unearthly howls from the top of the nearby hill. The coyote was the only animal he didn't think he would like as a pet. He felt the hairs rise on the back of his neck as their cries came again. He moved inside the cave and pulled his buckskin shirt a little tighter around him. Suddenly, inside the cavern, he heard a sound. Something was stirring, moving behind him.

'Who's that?!' he asked sharply.

A gentle voice answered, 'Do not fear, I am Bearwoman, who was once a woman and am now a bear. I will sit beside your fire with you and talk, if you will.'

The little Navajo looked into the shadows and suddenly he was able to see a large, dark shape ambling towards him.

'Peace be upon you, Bearwoman,' he said and smiled, for he was not the least bit frightened of her. She seemed so pleasant as she sat down before the fire.

'How did you get turned into a bear?' was his first question. Then he wondered if perhaps he should not have asked.

But Bearwoman began to tell him. 'I was a young woman in the prime of life and married to a brave warrior when my husband's enemies came one night and killed him. I was hidden under our bed-coverings,' she continued, 'so they didn't find me. When they had gone, I was crazed with grief. My husband's mother told me to be more courageous and not to be so weak, but I wept every night thinking of his death.

'One night he came to me in a wonderful ghost shape, smiling and showing me his bows and arrows, meaning that he was happy in the hunting grounds of eternity. But I still could not get used to his death and I became ill, not wanting to live. So my mother-in-law took me to a wise woman, to live with her until I became better. I found it even harder to be away from the place where I had lived with my husband. I tried to help the old woman as much as I could but she used to fly into a rage and scold me. At last I resolved to run away. I did not care if I lived or died. In fact I often wanted to die, but somehow the Great Spirit kept me on earth.'

'How long is it that you've been a bear and how did it happen?' asked the boy.

The bear nodded. 'I was just coming to that. It was a very long time ago — I cannot tell just how long. But one day, when the old woman was particularly bad-tempered, and had gone to get some herbs she needed to give me a medicinal drink, I ran away. I ran as fast as I could in the other direction, and soon I was far away from that horrible place. She was always giving me those herbal drinks and they tasted so bitter that they were worse than my illness. However, as soon as I got right away from her, I began to feel better and was able to live on the berries and nuts which I found everywhere in the woods. But I knew that the cold months were coming and I was without proper clothing or moccasins.

'That night I lay under the stars and, looking up into the sky, I said from deep in my heart, "O Great Spirit, Great Spirit, send me some help and keep me warm, for I know the cold weather is coming and I really do not want to die after all. I will wait until I hear your answer, Great Spirit. Do not desert me now, I pray."

'Then I threw myself on my face and waited. There was a rumbling in the distance as of thunder and the sky suddenly seemed to be full of lightning, and the rain began to fall as if the world would be flooded. I lay there waiting, shivering with terror. Then, all at once I lost consciousness and knew no more. When I came to myself it was morning. The birds were singing. The sun was bright and, as I stretched myself, I felt as warm as if I was covered from neck to toe in some thick fur robe. I looked down at myself. I was covered in fur! I had been turned into a bear. So Bearwoman I became. I do not know how many years ago that was. I often join real bears and live with them. They do not know of my human spirit. So I suppose I shall just have to remain like this forever, for I do not see any chance of my going to those happy hunting grounds reserved for warriors like my husband.'

Bearwoman stopped speaking and the little Navajo looked at her with sympathy. 'I lost my mother and father in the great hunger,' he said. 'And I have thought of running away, but where would I go until I am bigger and able to fend for myself?'

Bearwoman put her big paw on his arm and she spoke in her gentle voice, 'Do not run away, Navajo. I will be your mother until you are strong and I will advise you, for I know all you will want to know. Come here to this cave at any time when you are lonely or tired. Come here and I will comfort you and treat you as I would if you were my own son.'

And so it happened: until he was grown, the young Navajo visited his bear mother often, until he needed her no more. Then one day she said to him, 'I had a message last night in my dreams from the Great Spirit that I am to be reunited with my husband and my years of being Bearwoman are over.'

'Oh…! Well, thank you Bearwoman, thank you for all your help,' said the young Navajo, and touched the thick dark fur with a loving hand.

In that moment, the bear's fur vanished and before him stood a radiant young woman in a white buckskin dress, fringed and sewn with delicate beadwork, finer than any he was ever to see in his life.

'Thank you, my son,' she said, 'for all that you've meant to me during this time of waiting. Remember, I will always help you even though you will now see me only in your dreams.'

'Goodbye, Bearwoman!' he shouted as she vanished, and he remembered her for the rest of his life. When he grew to man's stature he became a great artist and painted many things, some from his memory and some from visions. Always, in the corner of each of his pictures, he painted a miniature likeness of a bear in her honour, until he too went to the happy hunting grounds at last.

Black Bull and the Magic Drum

ONCE UPON A TIME there lived a tribe who knew from the tales of their grandfathers and their grandfathers' fathers that they were called *The People*. Their tales told of how once, long, long ago, they had come from a place far away across the frozen waters in the north. And *The People* knew that they were very important in that far-away land. But there had been some great tragedy — their cities there were destroyed by famine and plague.

So now they lived in this country and called their collection of adobe mud dwellings 'The City'. They knew that one day, if the message came from the Spirits of the Upper World, which communicated through the bodies of birds, they would pack up all their belongings and go — back to that far-away land.

Their leader was called Black Bull and he had beside him at all times a drum — his magic drum, as the members of his family called it. This drum was one which received messages from the Upper World and told Black Bull what to do when his people faced problems. He had only to take the wooden drumstick in his right hand and roll his eyes up into his head, and the magic drum spoke loud and strong till the answer was given. Then it would stop, and the drumstick would drop out of Black Bull's hand and he would lie as if deeply asleep for at least an hour until the spirits from the Upper World had departed.

'Tell us, father,' his favourite daughter, Hazelwand, asked one day, 'if we came from so different a place to this, why did we not bring seeds of the crops which we grew in our old home with us?

Here we have only very ordinary Indian corn, the squash, the beans, the potatoes, the tobacco and the pumpkins of this new world.'

'Quite simply, my dear child,' replied Black Bull, 'we suffered many hardships on the way here. We lost some of our finest kinsmen. Many little ones were born on the way, and the old ones had to eat the seed that they had brought so carefully. There was a terrible shortage of food in the cold times along the way.'

'Have we anything left of the jewellery or the dresses which those early ones wore when they came into this land?' persisted Hazelwand, for though she had heard this many times before, she loved to hear it again.

'Yes, we have one of the old pieces of silver set with turquoise and amber and coral. And there are two of the shells which still remain from those early times sewn here into my belt,' said Black Bull.

'As you know,' he continued, 'the embroideries which your mother makes have just the same patterns as those on the saddle-bags of *The People* when first they came here. The blue zigzags are for the rivers that we crossed on our way here, and the white zigzags are for the snow on the top of the mountain of our ancient homes which touched the dwelling places of the Great Ones.'

'Yes, I remember,' she said, 'and the other designs like the clouds in the sky on a summer's day are the frozen breath from the guardian dragons that float above the mountain peaks, near to the Great Ones' abode.'

Hazelwand looked very dreamy, for she too liked to think of those fine embroidery designs which had come to her from her ancestors in the old land across the frozen sea and beyond. Gazing at the skyline, she imagined that the great jagged rocks so far above were those of *The People's* early home.

'Respected old one,' she said to her father, 'let me go and try to find that place so far away. Can I not get there the way that the first people came?'

'No, no, never!' cried Black Bull. 'You cannot find it, for it is not only days and days march away, it is also hundreds of years away. Believe me, my child, my favourite daughter, do not attempt it for you will only cause yourself and me great pain and suffering.'

'Very well, then I shall not say any more about it,' said the girl. But she carefully avoided her father's eyes and hoped that he would not notice that she had avoided promising that she would not go.

It was mealtime and Hazelwand was soon busy helping her mother with the food. That night the girl packed a few of her more precious belongings and. taking them in a small bundle, went to the house of the tribe's wise woman.

'Oh, Wise Woman of *The People*,' she begged, 'give me a charm to keep me safe when I go away to look for the country from which we came, for it pulls at my heart night and day and I will have no peace until I've seen it.'

'Daughter, daughter, curb your willful desires to travel alone on that long, long road. You will have to travel for a hundred years and even then you will never find it,' said the old woman fingering her long strings of medicine beads.

'Oh, Mother, I must go! Give me magic words to help me,' Hazelwand pleaded. 'If you do not help me, I will go without your magic and that will be dreadful for I will not feel protected.'

'Very well, then,' the old crone relented, 'may you be given the wisdom of the snake, the swiftness of the eagle, the strength of the she-bear, and the cunning of the fox. And may you walk in beauty — beauty to the right of you, beauty to the left of you, beauty above you and beauty below you. And never forget that you are of *The People.*'

Then she held her sacred charms over Hazelwand's head and closed her eyes, her lips moving silently. When she opened her eyes again the girl was gone. The old woman sighed and shook her head. Then, crossing her arms across her breast, she began to croon softly to herself, rocking backwards and forwards in her chair. Her house dog lifted up his head and howled.

When Black Bull heard of his daughter's departure, he at once took up his magic wooden drumsticks and began to play upon his drum. He drummed for hours, never for a moment drinking water or letting a morsel of food pass his lips. The wise woman sat in her house rocking backwards and forwards, backwards and forwards — muttering spells, shaking coloured sands upon a tray, making one magical design after another.

For two days and two nights they waited and there was no sign of Hazelwand's returning. 'I will bring her back,' said her father to *The People* who sat around him. They knew that she could never make her way through the dangers of the wild or find that far-away land which no longer existed, except in the imagination of *The People.*

Without food and without water for three days and three nights they sang in time to the beat of Black Bull's drum. On the morning of the fourth day, as the first streaks of dawn came into the sky, the drum of Black Bull grew louder until it drowned out all the voices of *The People.* Black Bull stopped, let the drumstick fall from his fingers and slumped forward onto his face for a short time. Then the tired and dusty figure of his favourite daughter came limping into sight, her eyes wild and her moccasins torn, her feet bleeding. Her mother rushed forward and supported her as she almost fell to her knees.

Hazelwand cried, 'Forgive me, I know now I was wrong. I will never leave you again.'

And Black Bull rose to his feet like a young warrior and smiled at her with proud joy and embraced her. She never told them what difficulties she had gone through in those three days, looking for the way to that far distant land. They never asked her but from that time forward until she married, Hazelwand did not leave her family again.

The magic drum often spoke at other times and in many different ways to help to heal the sick and give solace to the bereaved and the lonely. But Black Bull felt that it had never done better than when it brought his favourite daughter back to him, in obedience to the sacred wishes of the Great Ones: they in their wisdom knew that all men, even *The People*, had to abide by their decisions and wait for their directions in this life.

Golden Eagle's Magic Bag

ONCE UPON A TIME, not long after the arrival of the first white men, there lived in the high Dakota mountains a hunter called Golden Eagle. He was tall, and strong as a bear, cunning as a wolf, and skilled in the medicine of the Dakotas.

One day when he was visiting his traps, he found that he had caught a strangely beautiful fox, but as he was taking it out, the fox spoke in a human voice saying, 'Golden Eagle, set me free. I'm not an ordinary fox. Let me go and I will reward you one day when you shall have need of me.'

The animal looked at him so appealingly that Golden Eagle's heart was touched and even though he was sorry to lose such a fine pelt, he released the creature. Before it ran off the fox said, 'You will not be sorry that you have spared me, for I am an Enchanted One and I thank you for this kindness.'

Golden Eagle went to his next trap and there he found he had caught a wildcat. Expecting to have his hand bitten by the spitting cat, he put on a thick glove as he handled it, but to his great surprise the wildcat spoke in a human voice and said, 'Golden Eagle, let me go free. I am no ordinary animal. I am one of the Enchanted Ones, and if you release me I can be of service to you one day when you will have need of me.' Golden Eagle stared at the cat and asked, 'Are all the Enchanted Ones of the mountain in my traps today? I have only just set free a magical fox whose pelt I would dearly have loved to possess and now you too speak with a human voice. Surely the Great Ones are testing me with these remarkable happenings.' But he released the wildcat.

Then the wildcat said, 'Sometimes we take the form of animals and get caught like this, but not all hunters have your kind heart. Thank you, Golden Eagle. You will not regret this, I promise you.'

And with that the wildcat ran off and disappeared in the undergrowth.

That night, Golden Eagle returned to his lodge and told his wife what had happened as they ate their meal. Her eyes grew round in wonder at his story: 'Surely you are singled out by the Great Ones that they come to your traps and then offer you their services in exchange for their freedom,' she said, 'Blessed are the names of the Great Ones of the mountain.' And she sprinkled some magical herbs on the fire with words of gratitude.

Not far from Golden Eagle and his wife there lived a half-breed trapper called Pierre, who was a truculent man with a dark soul. He caught birds and animals to keep himself fed and clothed during the hard winter, and trapped for pelts which he took to the trading post in the spring. But it mattered not how hard he tried, he caught only the most puny animals. His skins were of little value, and he often cast envious eyes upon the rich pelts brought to the post by Golden Eagle. Many a time he had thought of raiding Golden Eagle's lodge while the hunter was away on one of his journeys far up the mountain.

One day he hid in the branches of a tree overlooking the lodge. Soon Pierre saw Golden Eagle say goodbye to his wife and go hunting. This meant that the young woman, Spotted Deer, was now alone. Pierre waited a bit longer until he was sure that the coast was clear, then he shinned down the tree and called, 'Oh Golden Eagle, are you there? It is I, Pierre, who wants to talk to you about the price of skins.'

Spotted Deer came out of the lodge and said gently, 'My husband is out hunting. He will not be back for some days. If you take that trail yonder, you should come upon him in a short while if you want to ask him something.'

'Ah, that is good,' said Pierre, and coming towards her, he caught her by the wrist. 'Now you shall give me all the best skins that there are here and at last I will have something good to take to the trading post.'

Poor Spotted Deer cried out and tried to call her husband's name, but Pierre tied some cloth around her mouth to silence her and tied her to a tree outside the lodge. Then he went in and began to pull out the best of all Golden Eagle's pelts. No sooner had he started to stuff the first into his bag than there was a wild cry, and a bunched-up ball of fur came hurtling at him from inside the lodge. A great wildcat with teeth bared and razor sharp claws attacked the evil half-breed, screaming as only wildcats can scream. Spotted Deer saw that Pierre's face and hands were covered with blood from gashes inflicted by the cat's claws and teeth as, covering his eyes with his hands, the trapper ran to escape from the infuriated animal.

Spotted Deer looked on amazed as the wildcat changed into a tall and radiant being dressed in a long, white buffalo-skin robe, whose face was so beautiful that she dared not look upon it. The figure raised its arms for a moment and Spotted Deer's bonds were loosened and the cloth tied over her mouth also fell away.

'Thank you, thank you, Great One,' stammered Spotted Deer, falling to her knees, but the figure raised her up with powerful hands and said, 'Your husband gave me freedom when I was caught in his snare. Now I have been able to save you in the same way. But do not think that we shall forget you humans. We will always be watching you. Give Golden Eagle this bag. When he puts his hand into it, he will find within it anything which he needs.'

Then the radiant being vanished and, on the ground beside her, Spotted Deer saw a finely embroidered bag of white buffalo-skin.

When Golden Eagle returned, he was amazed by his wife's story and examined the bag in wonder. However, the thought of Pierre's wicked action filled his heart with anger and he vowed to kill him if ever their paths should cross.

'No, no, husband. Do not think thoughts of murder,' Spotted Deer warned him gently. 'We must not do this thing. Let us try the magic bag and see what wonders it will perform.' Thus she turned her husband's mind away from dark deeds. Smiling, she handed him the magic bag.

'I will ask for a fine silver necklace set with turquoises for you, my dear wife,' he said putting his hand into the bag. 'If the distress you have suffered can be forgotten by this present, I will be glad.'

No sooner had he spoken than there appeared a beautiful necklace of silver with seven blue stones and he placed it round Spotted Deer's neck. They went into the lodge together. From that day forward, if Golden Eagle needed food, arrows for his bow or beads for his wife to sew on his new moccasins, all he had to do was wish and the magic bag gave him what he needed.

He lived happily with Spotted Deer for a year and a day and his joy was great when Spotted Deer put his newborn son into his arms.

'His name shall be Golden Deer,' said Golden Eagle, 'until the day when he chooses his own name.'

Winter came, snow covered the land and food was scarce, but the small family always had plenty for the magic bag provided all they required. One day, Golden Eagle was out hunting and the papoose was hanging in his warm, protective fur-lined cradle from the branches of a leafless tree. Spotted Deer was attending to the fire and singing to herself when something made her raise her head. Fear gripped her heart for Pierre, the half-breed, was once more standing before her with a leer upon his lips.

'Ha, ha! You stupid squaw!' he snarled. 'Did you think I wouldn't be back for those skins some day? Don't make a sound or I will shoot you dead and the papoose too.'

'Go quickly! My husband will kill you if he finds you,' cried Spotted Deer, putting her arms around her child. 'He's already overdue. Go, I beg you, and leave us alone, if you want to save your own life!'

But Pierre pushed her roughly to the ground and began to help himself to the furs. Looking around for something to put them in, he spied the white buffalo-skin bag. He was just about to pick it up when a fox ran between his legs, tripping him up, and Spotted Deer saw that the animal's fur glistened with a strange beauty. Suddenly the fox changed into a radiant being as tall as a pine tree, and Spotted Deer dared not look up.

There was a wild cry from the half-breed and he threw himself face down upon the ground.

'Do not be afraid, Spotted Deer,' said a voice. 'He is dead and will never trouble you again. Put your hand in the magic bag and wish for your husband — he will come at once.'

Then the bright radiance was gone and there was silence broken only by the crackling of the fire. Spotted Deer pulled the magic bag towards her and put her hand inside.

'Oh, Golden Eagle, come to me,' she cried.

Immediately, her husband stepped out of the bag and held her in his arms until she had told him the whole story. Without a word, he dragged the body of the half-breed away and buried it at the foot of the mountain. Then Spotted Deer and Golden Eagle took a meal from the magic bag, and little Golden Deer laughed and crowed with delight to see his father again.

The Great Ones never had cause to appear again, but they knew that as long as Golden Eagle had his buffalo-skin bag to provide whatever was needed, all would be well.

The Sleeper of the Cave of Darkness

ONCE UPON A TIME there lived a Navajo boy who had no brothers or sisters because they had died in the Great Hunger before he was born. Daily, his mother sent him to play in the hills, where he collected stones and pieces of wood to take back to her as presents. The boy was called Little Horse after his father, Spotted Horse, who had died. He was strong and active and loved walking for miles, which he did without feeling the least bit tired. His mother, Bright Water, was a talented weaver. She spent many hours making blankets and pieces of material so that she could sell them, and make a little money to keep herself and the child. Of course, if she had not been able to weave, the Navajos of the small village where they lived would willingly have shared their food with her, but Bright Water was proud and wanted to pay her way.

Little Horse was about eight years old when this story begins. He trudged off to the hills as usual to look for pieces of turquoise, or anything which might be used to make his mother a necklace. He walked and walked until he came to a place where he had never been before and, trying to climb a bit higher, he slipped and fell into a deep gully. Scrambling around to catch hold of a rock and haul himself up, Little Horse felt something give under him, and suddenly he found himself in a great cave.

It was dark in the cave but there was light somewhere in the furthest corner and so, blinking, Little Horse began to edge his way carefully towards it. To his surprise there was a further opening from where the light seemed to be coming. But just as he was about to step forward a voice, loud and terrifying, said, 'Who are you, boy, and why do you come here to disturb me in my age-long sleep?'

Little Horse was rooted to the spot. Before him was a small figure, no bigger than himself, seemingly an old man with a luminous white thatch of hair tied with a bright blue scarf, wearing a shining white robe sewn all over with glowing shells.

'Who…who are you?' stammered Little Horse, 'and how… how long have you been here?'

'I am the Father of Peace, the Sleeper of the Cave of Darkness. I have been here for many, many years, long before the Navajos came here, long, long before the white man came, and I will be here long after they and you have gone.'

White light played over his face and Little Horse felt ice-cold shivers down his back.

'I am sorry to have disturbed you, Father of Peace,' said the boy and backed away, but the spirit placed a hand upon his arm and he was frozen to the spot once more.

'Just come and visit me again whenever you can,' the old man said kindly. 'I would like to hear a human voice now and then, but not a man's or a woman's — only the voice of a young one. Come here as often as you like and I will give you a present each time you come.'

He put his hand into the pockets of his shining leather belt and gave Little Horse a luminous stone. As soon as Little Horse had thanked him, he waved farewell and vanished.

The boy found his way home as fast as he could and told his mother the story. She gazed in amazement at the stone the old man had given Little Horse, and saw that it was a fine opal. 'This would make me a wonderful pendant,' she cried and showed it to all her friends, telling them the whole story.

Now among the Navajos, there was one who was a greedy man. When Little Horse set off for the hills next day, he followed to see where the magical cave of the sleeper might be, so that he might get one of the beautiful stones for himself. He saw the cave into which the boy disappeared and went cautiously to the entrance, but although he heard voices he could see nothing. He concealed himself and soon Little Horse came out, his eyes shining with joy. He hopped and skipped all the way home to give his mother another present from the old man.

The greedy Navajo went into the cave with a burning piece of wood to serve as a torch and looked around. He saw nothing but stone walls as old as time itself. There was no sign of the old man of whom the boy had spoken — a being whom most of the villagers thought must be in the boy's imagination. But suddenly the old man appeared and said in his loud harsh voice, 'How dare you rouse the Sleeper of the Dark Cave, Father of Peace and custodian of the opals. Go! Leave this place and never come here again. May you forget that you have ever seen me or that I have spoken these words.'

The man dropped his torch and stumbled from the cave, his mind blank. He reached his own tent without knowing that he had ever been out that day and so the secret remained safe.

Time went by and one day Little Horse's mother was taken ill with a fever and though she was given all of the remedies the wise woman of the tribe produced, she seemed to be little better after a week. Tossing and turning in the wigwam, she even failed to recognise her son when he sat beside her and wiped her sweating face.

'Your mother seems to be hearing the voices of the spirits,' said the wise woman gently to the boy. 'It might well be that she will join your father in the Happy Hunting Ground before long.' She broke into a low chant of magical names sacred to the Navajos, and gestured to Little Horse to leave.

Without a word, the boy stumbled away towards the Cave of the Sleeper and though he did not show it, his heart was heavy with sorrow. He entered the dark cave mouth and walked towards the light at the far end.

'O Father of Peace,' he whispered, 'Let me speak to you. I need your help.'

As he finished uttering these words, the old spirit appeared and said, 'Ask anything of me, my child, I will certainly help you.'

'My mother is ill and I fear she may die. I do not want her to go to the Happy Hunting Grounds, for then I will be quite alone. I have no brothers or sisters and there is no one I love more than my mother. Save her, good spirit, and I will do anything you ask.'

'Will you give anything I demand, then, even if it is something quite important to you?' insisted the Father of Peace.

'Yes, anything, my arms or my legs, my eyes or my teeth,' said Little Horse, 'if only my mother could be restored to health.'

'Then go,' said the old spirit. 'You will find that she has recovered, but you will no longer be able to speak, for your voice will be gone. That is the price that you must pay for this favour.'

Little Horse nodded his head vigorously to show how pleased he was at the old spirit's pronouncement, and when the old man vanished, he ran as fast as his legs could carry him to his mother's side. He found her sitting up, being given a bowl of soup by the ancient crone, and though she took all the credit for it, Little Horse knew who was responsible for the miracle.

He was not able to speak again but felt that it was well worth the loss of his voice to have his mother better once more. Many remedies were given to him to try and bring about the return of his voice, but at last everyone grew used to the fact that Little Horse was dumb.

The years went by and Little Horse was looking for a wife, but it was not easy for him to find one. At last he fell in love with a beautiful maiden who was as kind-hearted as she was lovely, and the fact that he was unable to speak did not seem to worry her. When the day of his marriage came round and his bride appeared in her bridal dress, white-fringed and beaded, he wanted with all his heart to tell her how much he adored her, but he was reconciled to the inevitable.

Presents brought by the wedding guests were handed to him. Among them was a piece of birch bark, wrapped in a fragment of deerskin, upon which was burned with a red hot coal — AS A WEDDING GIFT I GIVE YOU YOUR VOICE. TELL YOUR WIFE WHAT YOU WISH TO TELL HER — FATHER OF PEACE.

Little Horse put his hand to his throat and touched it. Then he said in a fine voice, deep and strong, 'Blessings upon you, my wife, and greetings and blessings be to you all, my friends.'

There were cries of joy and congratulations from all, and Little Horse was the happiest man in all the land.

The Three Brothers

*T*HERE WERE ONCE THREE BROTHERS of the tribe of the Arapaho Indians who were tall, handsome and very skilled at hunting. But every time they went hunting the youngest brother always seemed to have the best luck. He brought in so many fine animals that his older brothers became very jealous of him.

'Let us kill Little Eagle,' said the eldest brother, Wild Bear, to the middle brother, Red Horse, 'and then the others will not laugh at us as they've been doing lately. By the moon and the stars, we two have suffered enough from their jeers and their sneers.'

'How shall we do it?' asked Red Horse, his eyes bright with excitement.

'Next time we go hunting let us take him further and further away,' said Wild Bear, 'and then when he's completely lost we will do what is necessary and no one else will ever know what happened. He could have been killed by an animal or fallen in a pit or something of the sort.'

The two wicked brothers awaited their opportunity, and soon it came. All the men of the tribe had gone out on a hunting expedition and the three brothers went together, as usual. The evil brothers pushed further and further after the quarry, drawing Little Eagle away from the rest of the tribe. Suddenly, when Little Eagle was concentrating hard on finding the animal's tracks, they both attacked him from behind and he fell senseless to the ground. But as they were about to kill him they heard the cries of the other members of the hunting party, and they hurried off in that direction to make it appear as if nothing had happened.

The brothers joined their fellows and told the others that Little Eagle had said he would go on alone and rejoin them later, as he was on the track of some wonderful animal.

Little Eagle lay where he had fallen, half hidden in bushes, till night fell but still he did not regain his senses — the clubs of Wild Bear and Red Horse had given him such a terrible beating. One of the Enchanted Beings who guide the affairs of men found him at last and brought him back to consciousness. But he was still badly injured and could not see, so the Enchanted Being guided his steps until he found himself by the tents of some friendly Indians.

These Indians were blood brothers of the Arapaho, and he spent many months with them. But he did not fully recover his memory and did not know his name or who he was, or what had happened to him. So he stayed on with his new friends, not knowing that his brothers had tried to kill him, and he was even accepted as a son by the old chief who felt sorry for him.

Time passed and Little Eagle regained his former strength, though not any knowledge of who he was, so he became known as Two Persons: the man he had been and forgotten and the man he now was.

In time, Two Persons made a name for himself, hunting with the young men of his adopted tribe. They liked him for his hunting prowess and praised him for it. They were not jealous and he was quite happy in his new life. Sometimes he did wonder who he was, though he knew he was an Arapaho because of the way the beads were sewn onto his shirt, his leggings and the small pouch that hung from his belt.

The chief had a daughter called Blue Stone and she was

always looking at Two Persons in the way a girl looks at a man whom she wants as a husband. She wished that he were of her tribe so that he might ask her to marry him, but that was impossible, for he was a nameless man with no tent of his own and no horse, someone who only went hunting with the young men because he was good at it. He helped to bring food to the tribe, and so could eat with the men without shame. And, though he felt much the same about Blue Stone, he felt powerless to approach her.

One night, the Enchanted Being which had taken care of him when he was lying badly wounded, came to him in a dream and said, 'I am your guardian from the nether world, and I say to you that you must no longer be a nameless one. Your name is Little Eagle and you are an Arapaho. Your people live in such-and-such a place and it is time to take a wife and return to them. Your brothers once wanted to kill you, but you will not now die at their hands.'

Little Eagle replied, 'O Enchanted One, I have nothing to offer a wife. How can I return to my people if my brothers feel like that about me?'

'Did you not hear me? I have said you will not die at their hands. Go, ask for your woman from her father, the chief, and I will make your way easy so that he will agree. Then you will return to your people and be happy with them once more and you will be a great hunter. As to the journey…' The Enchanted Being gave Little Eagle some further instructions and then disappeared, leaving him filled with joy.

Next day he went to the old chief and told him the whole story. He told him that he had remembered who he was and he asked for Blue Stone to be his wife, if she were willing. The chief knew his daughter's mind: he smiled and agreed. So Little Eagle took Blue Stone by the hand and they went to collect a few herbs as the Enchanted Being had instructed in his dream.

Little Eagle's home was far away, and the journey took a long time. When Little Eagle and Blue Stone got to the place where he had been born, it was to find that all his people were stricken by a strange illness. In after years, it was called The Spotted Sickness and was often painted by Indian artists, being one of the worst scourges they had ever suffered. It was in fact smallpox, which had been brought by some of the first white men to come to their land.

Little Eagle and his wife knew what they had to do. They boiled the herbs they had brought and gave the infusion to the stricken members of the tribe. Some lived and some died, but the medicine helped many to recover. Little Eagle's two brothers, Wild Bear and Red Horse, were so changed in appearance as to be almost unrecognisable. The illness had disfigured them badly and they begged Little Eagle to forgive them. They knew he had saved their lives with the medicine made from the strange herbs.

He forgave them, and as soon as they were well enough and strong again, they all went hunting together. They rejoiced in their hearts that they had not killed their brother, for they had felt the sting of conscience every day since they went back to search for him and found him gone. The Enchanted Beings looked after Little Eagle and preserved his life so that he became a great hunter until he went to the Happy Hunting Grounds at last.

The Singing Stones

RAINBOW MAIDEN WAS KNEELING and grinding her corn, thinking of nothing in particular. The sun was shining on her Zuni village and the hens were pecking at the odd grain of corn around her feet. Back and forth went the stones and Rainbow Maiden felt as if time were standing still. The corn was placed on the stone and another cube-like stone was rubbed over it with a rhythmic motion. She was singing to the stones as her mother and her sisters sang to theirs when, to her complete surprise, the stones began singing back to her.

The song of the stones was soft and low and marvellously sweet, and for a moment Rainbow Maiden stopped singing. She sat back on her heels, amazed at the wonder of it all, hardly able to believe her own ears. What the stones sang, she could not make out. There was a strange humming sound and the words of the song were all new to her, but very beautiful. After a while, she returned to her grinding, her ears still straining to catch every sound of the celestial music.

'Come! Stop your grinding. Come to the midday meal, my daughter,' came a call from inside, and Rainbow Maiden went to help her mother with the food.

As usual, her brothers and their young friends were playing flutes and drums, and dancing. But this time, Rainbow Maiden was in a daze and could not dance, for she was thinking of the singing stones and of the beauty of the music they made.

'What could it all mean?' she asked herself. And why were they singing to her? She knew that her mother's and her sisters' grinding stones were not like hers. She felt afraid to say anything about it in case everyone thought she was mad.

Next day, she began her grinding again, singing under her breath in rhythm with her work. She didn't expect more music from the stones, but no sooner had she begun than the beautiful singing started again. This time she could just make out the words, which went something like this:

'Rainbow Maiden, Rainbow Maiden, grind the corn, grind the corn. Soon you will marry the finest man born. Soon you will marry the finest man born.'

Blushing red to the roots of her hair, Rainbow Maiden said to the stones, 'Whom shall I marry and where is he from?' because she knew all the young men in the pueblo and didn't like any of them well enough to marry them.

'From far away, far away, with hair just like corn;
From far away, far away, with hair just like corn.'

'Nonsense,' said Rainbow Maiden. 'Just let me live here and be a happy maiden in my father's house. I don't want to marry anyone. Hair like corn, indeed! Whoever has hair like that?' and she tossed her head.

But she thought that she heard a merry, tinkling laugh from the stones, as they began to sing the same words over again.

With the coming of night the stones stopped their singing and she was honestly glad that there was an end to the refrain which they had sung all day. When she and her sisters and the other girls were dancing happily around the fire that evening, she was as light-hearted as any of them. But she couldn't help wondering if the stones were magic and really prophetic. Who was the strange man with yellow hair that she was to marry?

She had heard of some strange people with that kind of

colouring who had started coming to her part of the country and she thought that they must be very ugly indeed. She went to sleep happy and contented in the knowledge that the white men would never come to the Pueblo. Surely not!

The next day there was no more corn to grind and Rainbow Maiden was busy at her pottery for the rest of the week. She had all but forgotten the singing stones and their message. Then one day, when the sun was high in the sky and most people were resting after their midday meal, she saw some horsemen approaching at an easy pace. As they dismounted and led their horses closer, Rainbow Maiden saw that they were white men. There was much excitement and shouting between the Zunis and the white men, who could speak their language and used it well.

Round-eyed, Rainbow Maiden looked on as her father joined the other men in entertaining the strangers to a meal. Though the women remained in their own quarters, the news soon reached them that the head white man was a wise man of the Americans. Not only did he know the language of the Zunis, he also wanted to learn and write down the songs of their people. After the white men had been there for some hours, Rainbow Maiden was summoned by her father to meet the visitors. She was asked to sing the special rhythmic song that went with grinding corn and which she knew so well. To her surprise, as she looked towards the white man she saw that his looks were not at all horrible as she had feared. As he took off his hat and mopped his brow, her heart became his, for she realised that his hair was like corn silk.

So this was the man she was to marry. She sang her song and made to turn away, but she found a pair of admiring blue eyes were holding hers as she did so. Dr. Arthur McKenzie, the anthropologist, watched the slim Zuni girl return to her house; with a steady hand he copied out the notes she had left vibrating in his mind.

'What wonderful luck,' he thought to himself, 'that I should find all this good material here for my book on the Pueblo people.'

He thanked the old chief and asked permission to stay on a few days more. This was graciously granted and Arthur McKenzie had much work to do during the following week, writing down everything which would be of use in keeping the Zuni songs and age-old traditions alive. On the last night of his stay, Arthur McKenzie found himself looking again and again at Rainbow Maiden. It grieved him to think that he would soon be gone, and that he would never see her again.

He had built himself a farmhouse not far from the Little Colorado River and all he lacked was a wife to sustain him during the long months and perhaps years of writing his book on the Zuni songs and their history. He decided to speak out, and he did so to Rainbow Maiden's father.

'Will you let me have your daughter in marriage?' he asked. 'I will look after her well and she shall have all she desires, if she comes to my house.'

'Which daughter?' enquired the old man. Yet his eyes were smiling into McKenzie's own as if he knew the answer already.

'That one,' blurted out McKenzie. And Rainbow Maiden stood stock still before him, her heart as happy as a bird flying in the sky.

'Will this not be a surprise to her?' persisted the father. 'Is it not something of a shock, my child?' And he turned to Rainbow Maiden as if he must be sure that she wanted to go with the white man.

'The magic stones told me all about his coming, father,' she cried. 'I am sorry to leave you, but I will not be far away. He's told me about his house, and I know I will like it there.'

'Magic stones? What stones?' asked the father. 'What sort of medicine is this? Are you out of your mind, daughter?'

Rainbow Maiden cried out, 'No, no, I'm not mad. I heard my grinding stones promise me that a man with hair like corn would marry me. My stones sang to me for a long time before he came, and said that he was the best man ever. It is good medicine, father. I promise you that.'

She held out her hands to Arthur McKenzie: he took her wrists and placed on each of them a fine silver bracelet with a turquoise set in it. After blessings had been called down upon them by her father, they were accepted as man and wife by her family and by the tribe.

There was a great feast in honour of the young couple, and Rainbow Maiden's people all sang their songs to her husband for the rest of that long and happy night.

The Dog and the Bear

HERE ARE BEARS OF MANY COLOURS and sizes, yet there is only one bear of which I tell. There are dogs of many colours and sizes, yet there is only one dog of which I tell. Now gather round in the firelight and I will tell you what I mean.

Long, long ago when there were not so many stars in the sky and the winds blew in other directions than they do now, there lived a large black bear. He was tall and strong, wild and gentle, fat in the fall, thin in the springtime when he woke from his long sleep; and he loved honey more than anything else in the world. He walked with his toes turned in and his nose turned out and he was a great warrior. He had never seen men nor could he ever have imagined them — the first time he had heard about them was from a dog.

The bear was wandering about in his usual way looking for nuts and sniffing the air now and again to see what there was in the wind, when he smelt the dog smell. He had met dogs before but usually they were in packs and he did not like them. At other times he had driven them away by standing on his hind legs and growling menacingly, but this dog seemed alone and friendly. It was a large brown dog with a thick coat and a huge, bushy tail. He came towards the bear with much humility, his body low to the ground, tail wagging, his head turning from side to side, licking his chops almost apologetically. The bear stood still, watching the dog approach.

'Greetings be upon you, brother bear,' said the dog. 'May I

join you, for I am a stranger in this lonely place? I was brought here by a man, a hunter of the human kind who was taken by some strange fever. Though I waited beside his body for three days, he did not get up again. Soon, others of the human kind came: I hid myself and saw them put his body in some wrappings and then he was gone from my sight. I'm very hungry, for the humans, instead of giving me food, threw stones at me when I approached their fire at night. I've been running wild these last three days.'

'Welcome, brother dog,' said the bear. 'You will join me in hunting then, and we shall share whatever we can find. I like honey and nuts and anything which smells good. What do you like to eat?'

The dog stood up on all four legs, raising himself from the earth, and stretched in the warm sun. 'I catch and eat rabbits and small things like that and enjoy fresh red meat,' said the dog.

'Well, to each his own,' said the bear and went on with his own search.

The dog and the bear began to live together in the same cave, each catering to his own desires, and for some time they were as happy as the day was long. Time passed and the bear began to prepare for the winter, eating vast quantities of fruit and nuts to sustain him during his long hibernation period. The dog grew apprehensive about what would happen to him when his friend retired to the depths of the cave and went to sleep.

'I was thinking that it is time that I went in search of a new master,' said the dog. 'I have lived so long with the human kind, having one of their very best examples as an owner, that I am tempted to go near one of their settlements and choose myself another.'

'Do please go, brother dog,' replied the bear. 'I wish you would, for soon I shall not be able to be with you at all, and we will not meet again until the spring, when I shall come to full awareness again.'

'Very well, brother bear,' said the dog, taking leave of his friend. 'I will go and leave you in peace and when the snows have gone and the corn begins to sprout, I will come and seek you. Goodbye. I promise I will not forget you.'

The bear nodded sleepily and rather slowly turned and sought the depths of his cave. So the dog took the trail alone and travelled mile after mile, day after day, resting at night and catching food for himself on the way, until he reached a settlement. Being a young and powerful dog, he was looked upon quite favourably by several of the young men, and one hunter called Silver Knees chose him to be his hunting dog.

The dog liked his new master and soon they were a good team. As the weather grew colder, the dog was glad of the fire and the blanket which Silver Knees sometimes allowed him to crawl under.

'Silver Knees,' said his wife, River Moon, one day, 'I wish you could bring me a bear skin the next time you go hunting. I think I am the only woman in the tribe who has not got one. I have given you a son recently — I beg you to grant my request.'

'I shall remember your wish,' said Silver Knees. 'You will not need to ask me again.'

As soon as the spring came, Silver Knees prepared himself for the hunt. All winter he had been sharpening his knives and making himself new arrows with specially strong shafts. He asked the medicine man of the tribe to secure him immunity from the spirit of the bear he was to kill, and the medicine man did so:

'When you kill the bear you must be sure that you boil the

bones most carefully so no fragment of meat remains on them. The bear's bones must be tied together and wrapped in deer skins, then placed on top of a high platform. No part of the bear's skeleton may touch the earth, nor must it be dishonoured or disgraced.'

Silver Knees promised to do this and his wife started to prepare the deer skins for the wrappings. Then, with his provisions on his back and everything he needed, Silver Knees said goodbye to his wife and set off to look for the bear. He travelled for several days, camping at night beside the river, until he was near the spot where the dog had lived with his friend, the bear.

'The man is going to kill my brother bear, that I know,' said the dog to himself. 'How am I going to prevent this?' And his heart was heavy at the thought of what was to come.

When they were near the mouth of the cave which the dog knew so well, the man stopped and hung all his provisions and his blanket in the fork of a large tree, well above the ground. Then he said to the dog, 'You stay here on guard until I return. I have to look for bear tracks and I know by the signs that there is one somewhere nearby.'

The dog lay down under the tree and the man disappeared into the undergrowth. As soon as he was alone, the dog crept to the cave to see if he could find his old friend. He went in cautiously, looking from side to side and using his nose. Suddenly, he was on to the bear's scent and found him lying in a depression in the rock.

'My dear brother,' cried the dog. 'How wonderful to see you again after all these months. Did you have a good winter?'

'Yes, indeed,' answered the bear. 'It went so fast that I did not realise it was already spring. What a good feeling it was to wake up a few days ago and taste my first meal of spring.'

'Brother,' said the dog hesitantly, 'I am afraid I am the bringer of bad news. My new master is on the track of a bear to please his wife and I beg you to go away from here with as much speed as you can, as I am going to have to track you for him to kill.'

'Well, thank you for telling me,' said the bear. 'I shall put as much distance as possible between myself and this specimen of the human kind as quickly as I can. But it is a pity that I shall not have your company. It is something I have looked forward to, for you promised you would return in the spring.'

'I am deeply sorry,' said the dog, 'but I am now not as wild as you and I regret it. It is a long, long time since my blood and those of my forebears was pure wolf-blood. It has been contaminated by the tame dogs of men so I shall have to say goodbye to you, hoping that I have been able to save your life for the sake of our old friendship.'

Sorrowfully, the dog crept out of the cave. When his master returned he led him far away, pretending to find a bear scent in a totally different direction. By the time the man discovered that the dog was on a false trail, the bear was well away. He had gone into the river for some miles upstream, so that the scent was lost. The bear knew a thing or two about the river. It had saved him often from swarms of angry bees when he had robbed the wild hives of their honey, for his nose and eyes were always washed clear of the stinging insects as soon as he submerged himself in its deep waters.

The man was very angry with the dog at having lost him valuable time and he beat the animal with a leather thong. After trying to find another bear in many other directions, the hunter at last decided to return home. When he did so it was to be upbraided by his wife in no uncertain terms.

'How shall I keep up my head among the other wives of the tribe?' she cried. 'And I the mother of your son! Does that mean nothing to you? Shall the people say that Silver Knees is like a woman, that he cannot find a bear when he goes by himself?'

The man sharpened his knife again and sat at his meat, cutting himself a piece of dried venison. His anger made him lash out at the dog: 'It was because of this useless cur that I lost the bear. I knew there was one there. I smelt him and I saw his tracks. The dog made me think he was in the other direction. By myself, I would have caught that bear.'

The dog put his tail between his legs; his heart was broken because he had let the man lose faith in him and he longed for forgiveness. But a great hatred grew in the man's heart for the dog. Silver Knees would not even let the dog approach him, and did not feed him for two days and nights. When the dog tried to creep near to lick his hand the man, still nursing his wrath, threw stones at the dog and said, 'I was a fool to take you in, a stray and a no-good cur. Go back to whence you came and I will be well rid of you indeed. Go away! Back to the wilderness, for you are no hunting dog nor will you ever make one!'

A stone caught the dog on its rump and he ran blindly from the settlement. For several days and nights, the dog fended for himself, sorrowful in the knowledge that he was once more without a master, once more a loner. Little by little, he made his way back to where the bear lived.

As soon as the bear saw the dog, he raised his snout and looked anxiously around. He did not trust the other animal, fearing that the hunter was somewhere near. But the dog told him the sad tale of his downfall and the bear nodded in sympathy.

'Put not your trust in those of the human kind,' he said, 'for how in the world can they understand the freedom of the wild ones of the forest and the river, like ourselves? Come, join me here. We lived last year in perfect harmony, you eating your food and I mine, as we free creatures have done this many a year since time began.'

The dog agreed and thanked the bear for forgiving him for deserting him in the first place. And the blood of the wolf rose again in the dog so that he found himself stronger than ever before, and he moved freely in the wild till the end of his days.

The Fair Mohican

IN THE SEVENTEENTH CENTURY people from all over the world were flocking to America. They came by boat in their thousands, hungry for land and adventure. In many cases they were befriended by the Indians, and even today many Americans say with pride that they have an ancestor from the Algonquins or the Mohawks or the Sioux; but there were many clashes.

In 1637, John Mason from Norfolk marched into Indian country with a force of three hundred colonists and Mohican Indians. He destroyed the fortress of the Pequots, who had once been friendly towards the newcomers in that area, which is called Connecticut. Thus they became enemies.

This is the story of what happened following that raid. John Mason, after his six years in the new land, was able to talk many of the Indian dialects, and when a young woman dressed in the Mohican manner begged for help to escape from the battlefield, he allowed her to ride behind him on his horse to his army's nearest encampment.

'Thank you, White Hair,' she said as he gave her into the care of one of the women who looked after the kitchens. She looked with great interest upon the white man's fair curls, which peeped out from under his cap of raccoon fur.

'I will remember this forever,' she said. Her pale oval face was very beautiful. With a smile, John Mason rode off and hurried back to the battle-field to help with the wounded and to arrange for the burial of the dead. The Mohican girl had been tall and slim, with fine features and long black, shiny braids hanging on either side of her head. As he went on with the dreadful task of clearing bodies from the battlefield, cheering the wounded and keeping up the spirits of those who were helping him, John's mind kept returning to the face of the beautiful captive. That night he went from campfire to campfire hoping to see her, but was unsuccessful. Tired and hungry, he sat down, lit his own fire and settled back with a piece of dried meat from his pack.

The moon was full. The settlers had their wagons drawn into a large circle against attack by Indians. Their campfires were burning here and there as both settlers and soldiers prepared for the night. Suddenly, John's instinct made him look round and there, behind him, in the shadow of a huge tree was the beautiful Mohican girl. She stood straight and proud, her eyes looking boldly into his. Her feet in their embroidered moccasins made no sound as she approached him.

He got up and gestured to her to sit beside him on the rough blanket. Gracefully, she settled herself with her knees under her and took the piece of meat he offered on the blade of his knife. For a few moments they sat without speaking.

'I have been looking for you,' he said pleasantly. 'What have you been doing all day?'

'Everything which has been demanded of me by the white woman who feeds the soldiers,' she answered. 'I am glad to help. I am far from my own people and will never return to them.'

'What is your name?' he asked, chewing away. His pleasure at seeing her again was obvious to the girl. She beamed at him.

'Night Star,' she answered. 'I was born when my mother was alone in the wigwam where she gave birth, after my father had been killed by a snake. She came out of the wigwam with me in her arms to give me a first bath in the river, and looking up she saw the brightest star she had ever seen. So she gave me that name. I was taken captive by the people from whom you rescued me, and I am now your slave. You saved my life, White Hair, and you must now be responsible for me.'

'Oh come now,' laughed John, his blue eyes smiling into hers with charm and gaiety. 'You do not mean to say that you want to come to work for me just because I gave you a ride on my horse in the middle of today's battle. Oh no, Night Star, I do not need a slave. I can look after myself after all the years I've been alone in America.'

The girl replied earnestly, 'You have no woman to chew the skin for your moccasins, to embroider the shirt for your feast day, to take your horse to water when it needs to drink. I will do all these things for you, for I am an orphan with no father or mother, and no husband. I was far from my own people when I reached marriageable age, and I will become your woman if you do not think I am too ugly for you. I never loved a man before.'

John Mason laughed again and said, 'My dear Night Star, you're welcome to look after my horse for I am sure you know how, but I can assure you, dear girl, that I do not need you for any of the other things you describe. If I need new moccasins, I can buy them. As for my shirts, you can see I wear the one my mother made me of the purest Irish linen. That will last me for many a day yet. All I need is for someone to wash it now and again and hang it up to dry while I am asleep.'

'You saved my life and if you will have me with you, by the Great Spirit, I will be true and loyal to you even though you are a white man,' said Night Star firmly, expertly feeding the fire with more wood.

'I am very tired,' said John. 'I must get some sleep. Look, have this blanket of mine. Use it to wrap yourself in, and sleep here beside this tree. Look after my horse when I give it into your charge. I'll take you on as my guide and friend and you shall return with me to my own home when I go there one day.'

Night Star's eyes were shining with joy when she heard these words, for he had given her the blanket, which in her tribe meant that he wished to marry her. She seized his hand and kissed it fiercely.

When John Mason returned to the place where he had settled across the river, he found that it had been burned down by Indians. There was nothing for it but to build another house. All that spring, John and some of his friends from a neighbouring settlement laboured to build a home for himself and Night Star. They had now decided that they would get married.

A wandering preacher married them before they entered the house and they lived together for many happy years. When at last Night Star gave birth to John's son, she was happy when he said to her, 'My dear wife, our child will go to England and become an educated man, for I have my family there and they will use what money I have to send him to Oxford. He'll be a credit to both of us.'

Night Star's heart beat with pride as she said, 'I do not care if he can't even write his name, as long as he is as good a man of the woods as you are, White Hair.' And with a gentle finger she smoothed the fair stubble on the head of her child, which was as blond as his father's curls.

That is the story of Night Star, the fair Mohican, and how she became the wife of John Mason. Today, the family descended from them, point with pride to the embroidered moccasins which she made for her beloved White Hair, in those days long ago when the bison roamed. They know that he and she are now in the Happy Hunting Grounds where the Great Spirit told Night Star she would go with her Englishman when she died at last.

The Trail to the West

'WE HAVE ACQUIRED THE WHOLE of the territory formerly owned by Napoleon Bonaparte,' said President Thomas Jefferson in 1803. 'I sent a mission to Paris to try and buy the port of New Orleans, for the simple reason that I thought the place would be more prosperous in American hands, and bless me if I wasn't offered the entire Louisiana territory for fifteen million dollars.'

'But, sir,' said his private secretary, Meriwether Lewis, 'whatever does old Napoleon need all that money for? I agree that it is nothing but a very considerable wilderness at the moment, but it is still quite a bargain.'

President Jefferson laughed. 'He needs the money because he's involved in a war against the English, and I wish him luck, for fighting the English can be a pretty tricky business as we know.'

This transaction became known as the Louisiana Purchase and through its completion the then American territories were more than doubled in size. The one difficulty, as Meriwether Lewis saw it, was how to get the new area mapped efficiently. He asked the President to whom he thought the job could be entrusted.

'My good fellow,' said Thomas Jefferson, placing his hand on his secretary's shoulder, 'there's only one man for the job and that is my considered opinion.'

'But who is it, sir?' enquired Meriwether Lewis, quite innocent of guile.

'Why you, sir, of course, you big booby,' said the President. 'Oh no, you needn't blush. Next to myself, you're the only man, that I can trust with this difficult business. You are an army officer; you know how to make maps, chart territories and order supplies. I expect you to do it with your usual style.'

'Mr. President, sir, it is a very great honour,' said Lewis, 'and a great adventure, I know that. I shall have to have an aide, sir, and, if you agree, I will take my old friend, Captain William Clark, in that role.'

'Done,' said the President. 'Take as many men as you need in your party. All the arrangements will be in your hands. Go then, and may God bless you. If this is a successful trip, as I pray it may be, you will very likely have a place in the history books.'

President Jefferson was right, for the great adventure of Meriwether Lewis and William Clark is one of the more colourful chapters in the history of America.

They set off in the spring of the year 1804 with a party of some forty-three men. They took with them everything they would need for at least a year, or at most eighteen months, for they knew the way would be hard and quite uncharted. They hoped to cover a considerable distance during the long summer and fall, especially as they planned to go most of the way by boat. They had stared death in the face too many times to be scared of the wilderness and were cheerful as they set out in strong boats up the Missouri River, starting from a point near what is now the city of St. Louis.

The spring passed, and still they headed north and then westward up that great river, pulling and hauling their boats upstream. They hunted for animals along the way, so as to conserve their stocks of flour and fat. They had to be very careful always to husband their salt, for without it they would have found it very difficult to prepare food. The summer passed and then it was the glorious fall, and in that Indian summer they made further progress. But, as they knew from earlier army manoeuvres in America, once the long, hard winter set in there was nothing to do but make camp and wait.

Lewis and Clark were in somewhat of a quandary as to where they should stop. At last, they made camp in what is now North Dakota Territory. They met no other people during that long, hard winter but managed to survive well. Each man knew how to hunt, trap, and maintain his own equipment. When April of 1805 came, the party were fit and well, and raring to go. They grouped themselves around their captain and waited for instructions.

'Now fellows,' said Meriwether Lewis, 'we must find ourselves a guide, for here we are getting into really tough country. Let's get started, but keep your eyes peeled for any Frenchman or trappers who could help us on our way and save us from squandering valuable time, walking in the wrong direction.'

The men agreed and were overjoyed when, the very next day, they hailed a small party of hunters. It was soon arranged that one of them, a French Indian with a young Shoshoni wife, would go with them to show them the trail to the West. In fact the wife, whose name was Sacagawea, knew the trail better than he did.

Sacagawea led them across the Montana plains, her baby in its birch bark and leather cradle on her back, then over the tremendous Rocky Mountains, and at last, to the great Columbia River, which races and tumbles down the western side of the continental divide to meet the mighty Pacific.

She had led them safely through Indian territory, arranging for them to get horses and supplies from her brother, a promising Shoshoni Chief. When they parted from her, it seemed as hard to do as if she had been their own sister. Lewis and Clark promised the Indian girl that, when he grew up, they would arrange for her child to be sent to the East and educated as she had begged them to do.

In November 1805, they built Fort Clatsop on the Pacific Coast. They were the first Americans to travel from coast to coast across the land and make the road along which, later, so many thousands were to flow west. The two captains spent the whole of that second winter making their maps, drawing plans and pictures of the scenes through which they had passed. It had taken them two whole years.

A great deal of the credit must go to the Shoshoni maiden Sacagawea, who was their faithful guide. Nor must we forget the part played by her papoose, who travelled that way too, safely carried on the back of his courageous mother. Sacagawea had made the journey solely for the baby's sake, so that he should receive the white man's education and be a credit to his race.

TALES FROM ARABIA

The Tale of Hatim Tai

*O*NCE UPON A TIME long, long ago, there lived in Arabia a most kind and generous King called Hatim Tai. In his stables were the finest stallions and mares, in his tents the most beautiful carpets, in his army the bravest fighting men. Songs of his many generous deeds in war and peace were sung from one end of his dominions to the other, accompanied by tambours and flutes.

In the whole of that part of Arabia which came under his control, all men were brothers and all women sisters of their monarch, Hatim Tai. Children came running to him when he passed through the lines of their tents, and as soon as they were old enough, boys begged to join his elite corps of camel riders, formed to bring news from far distant regions to the court of Hatim Tai.

There was food for every mouth in the whole land, much treasure in the coffers and many rich oases for travellers and merchants. Every man had the right to stop the King when he rode upon his milk-white mare, Jamila, and to ask a favour — which was always granted, whatever it might be.

'Oh, Hatim Tai,' the supplicant would cry, pulling at his royal cloak, 'I beg a boon.'

And the King always stopped, and listened, smiled gently and granted the request. From far and wide came visitors to eat at his feasts, sit upon his priceless carpets and gaze on the numbers of his fighting men, with their long spears, their glittering daggers, their tremendous size.

But there was one who was jealous of Hatim Tai — another King with lands bordering upon his own. His name was Jaleel and he sent his herald to the King with this message:

'I am mightier and bolder than you will ever be, O Hatim Tai, and lord of many more tents and men. Therefore I want to possess myself of your lands, your people and all that you own. So tell me when we shall do battle, and all our young men shall be tested at that time. My warriors will certainly destroy yours, for we have many horses and spears, and you shall be as nothing after the fight which will ensue.'

Around him, Hatim Tai's viziers and emirs raised their hands to heaven and declared that they and all Arabians under his flag would fight to the death to preserve him and his family, whatever the cost in blood. The armed men took up the cry and came thronging to his tent, demanding to know the hour of the battle.

But Hatim Tai thought for a few moments, then he shook his head. 'Brothers,' said he, 'this is not your fight. I will not have battle joined for such a trivial matter as my life. I shall disappear into the mountains and the conqueror can then enter these dominions without killing a single living thing. You will not suffer nor will children lose their fathers, for it is my life that King Jaleel wants. He will not do anything except ride in here and take up his position in my tent, and that I will gladly give up to him. For I can live as a dervish, a wanderer without any of the trappings of the court, as many another has done before me.'

So, wrapping up some dates and nuts in a small sack, he said farewell to all his family and walked away.

King Jaleel, the conqueror, came in great state with much blowing of trumpets and beating of drums, and took over the entire country of Hatim Tai.

Some time passed during which the new King searched far and wide for Hatim Tai, but no sign of him was to be found. There was not one man, woman or child in all that vast area who would have betrayed the lonely King in his hiding place. Many went by night to take him food and help him in every possible way.

At court with his advisors, King Jaleel sat surrounded by much luxury and beauty, boasting of his conquest.

'Men of Arabia,' he shouted,' I took this country without one person raising a hand against me, without shedding one drop of blood. That coward Hatim Tai dared not show his face to me and is now hidden from view or is running still, I have no doubt,' and he laughed loudly, applauded by all his followers.

He saw the downcast face of one of Hatim Tai's advisers who was also at the festivities and cried, 'And what have you to say, O Wise One, about the cowardice of this late monarch of yours who is behaving like a woman?'

The man spoke out bravely, 'O King, our monarch Hatim Tai is the most generous man in the world. He told us not to fight but to let you enter these dominions unchallenged so that we would live. He went away to give us that chance. Though my life be forfeit, I must say this.'

The new King was nonplussed. Here was Hatim Tai doing something generous again, so that the people thought more of him than of their new ruler. Whispered tales about Hatim Tai's deeds were still circulating. Nothing good had yet been said about Jaleel, his spies told him.

How could he capture the hearts of his new subjects? He got very angry and ordered it to be proclaimed that whosoever could capture Hatim Tai and bring him to the court would be given many bags of gold.

But this made Hatim Tai's loyal subjects even more determined to save their King from the tyrant, and no hint of where Hatim Tai was hiding was given to those who sought him.

One day, when a very old couple was collecting firewood near the fugitive's cave, they began talking to each other. And Hatim Tai, watchful as ever when he heard voices, could not help listening.

'If only life were not so hard,' said the ancient man. 'The new King makes so many demands upon us, taxing us so cruelly and taking all the boys into his army. There seems to be less and less wood here. What shall we do when it is all gone?'

'Find Hatim Tai and get the bags of gold then, husband,' said his shrewish old wife. 'I hear that they have increased the reward money this very day. Why, we could live to the end of our days in great comfort if we were to turn him in.'

At that moment Hatim Tai stepped forward and said, 'Then you shall live in comfort for the rest of your days. Take me to the King and say no more about it.'

'Oh, generous Hatim Tai,' cried the old man. 'Never in a million years, even if I were truly tempted by all the houris of paradise, would I betray you. My wife is an old fool. Forgive her, good Hatim Tai.'

While they were arguing, several of Jaleel's soldiers came up and seized them all. They were brought before the King and Hatim Tai said,

'Your Majesty, give this old woodcutter the money for my discovery, for it was he who found me.'

In great dismay, the old man told how Hatim Tai had offered himself so that they would be comfortable for the rest of their lives.

King Jaleel was so amazed at this grand gesture of generosity that he decided to make a generous gesture too. He bade Hatim Tai return to his royal tent, embraced him as a brother and returned to his own country, taking his soldiers with him and promising to live in peace for all his days.

And Hatim Tai, too, lived in peace until he was called to paradise.

The Princess, the Vizier and the Ape

ONCE UPON A TIME in the land of Arabia there lived a King's daughter. Now this Princess, whose name was Kulthoom, loved the Prince of a neighbouring kingdom, but the chief vizier of her father's court loved her. The King knew nothing of this and looked to the day when he would marry his daughter to the monarch of another country. The chief vizier became so enamoured of Princess Kulthoom that he could not bear to think of anyone else marrying her.

Taking thought, he devised a cruel plan. He went to the King and said, 'Your Majesty, I have looked at the horoscope of the Princess and I fear that it is full of dread tidings.'

'How so?' asked the King.

'By the configuration of the signs and the planets at the moment of her birth, if she should marry there could be only tragedy,' said the vizier.

'Explain further,' said the King.

'If your daughter has children, they will be the cause of your Majesty's death,' said the vizier.

The King was aghast. 'What shall I do?' he asked.

'I can suggest a way of disposing of the Princess,' said the vizier. 'Place the poor young lady in a large chest. Put her jewels in with her and entrust the chest to the swift-flowing river, Almighty Allah will protect her.'

Eventually, the King agreed and the finest chest ever seen was made to contain the Princess and her jewels.

Now, the Princess's old nurse had overheard the King and the vizier talking and she told the Princess the whole story. At once, Princess Kulthoom wrote a letter to the Prince who loved her and told him of the plan to cast her upon the waters. The Prince was out hunting with his falcon on his wrist when the messenger came, but he left his sport immediately and thought of a way to save her.

He called his servants and gave them orders. Then he sent a letter to the Princess saying, 'Have no fear. Let them put you in the chest. I shall save you, with the help of Allah.'

The King and the vizier took the Princess, who had been given a draught of a magical brew to make her sleep, and placed her in the chest with her jewels. Within a few moments, the richly carved wooden chest with the Princess inside was floating away towards the distant sea. But no sooner had the chest gone a certain distance than the servants of the Prince brought it safely ashore with fishing nets. Carrying the sleeping Princess and her jewels to a cave, the prince and his servants placed a huge and ugly ape inside the chest and once more cast it upon the waters.

The servants of the vizier were waiting with their master at the next bend of the river. They took the chest out onto the bank and the vizier said to them, 'Take this to my secret hideout and let no one open it,' for he thought he had the Princess in his power and would soon bend her to his will. So the servants carried the chest away to the vizier's house in the mountains, while he himself went to tell the King that he would be absent for a few days on family business.

While the Princess was journeying in a silken palanquin to her new home, the vizier was approaching the chest with much joy.

'Oh, most beauteous Princess,' said he in considerable excitement, 'come to me and let us be happy here, together for ever.'

He opened the chest and out stepped, not the beautiful Princess Kulthoom but a grey and repulsive ape. 'Allah have mercy upon me,' cried the vizier. 'What magic has been used here? Who could have foreseen that putting the Princess in this chest and casting it upon the river could turn her into this fearsome shape?'

He knew there were many powerful magicians at court who were his enemies so he blamed one of them. He sent for fruit and fed the ape, who was very friendly and seemed to understand everything he said.

'Princess,' said he, 'I will look after you and keep you here in the style to which you have been accustomed until you regain your human shape.'

He gave up his position at court to attend to the ape and wait for the time, which he was sure would come, when the creature turned back into the Princess Kulthoom.

In the neighbouring kingdom meanwhile, the wedding of the Prince and Princess was celebrated with much rejoicing, and the Princess sent a message to her father telling him of the plot and its happy outcome. And all lived happily ever after — except of course the vizier.

The Deaf Brother
and the Blind Brother

ONCE UPON A TIME there were two brothers called Wahid and Ra'oof. Wahid was mostly blind and Ra'oof was all but deaf and one day they went to a big feast. After it was all over they began to make the long journey home.

'The dancing was bad,' said the blind man.

'Yes, the music was awful, too,' said the deaf one.

They walked on and on in the hot sun until suddenly, in a deserted spot, they came upon a donkey. It had such an appealing look that the deaf brother took up its halter and it followed them. It brayed several times in joy at having a master again, for its aged owner had died somewhere in the wilderness and it had been wandering alone for many days.

They all sauntered on until suddenly Wahid, the blind one, bumped into a huge mass of something, stubbing his toe.

'Oh, ouch, ouch, ouch,' he yelled. 'Whatever is this?'

Ra'oof, the deaf one, shouted at him, 'it's an old tomb with two locusts sitting on top, brother. Let's tie them in the corner of my handkerchief. You never know when they might come in useful.'

So the two locusts, the donkey and the brothers set off for their village once more. All at once, there came a great rainstorm. The thunder banged like the treasure chests of King Suleiman, rattling up in the mountains of Qaf which are supposed by the Arabs to surround the earth, and the lightning flashed as never before.

'Oh,' said the blind man, 'the lightning is not too bad, but the thunder is really dreadful.'

They ran for shelter to a large, ruined building which had at one time been a caravanserai. But no sooner had they closed the door of the only room still left standing than seven magical ogres appeared, banging on the door to be let in from the storm. The deaf man was not frightened because he could hear very little. The blind man went to the door and shouted, 'Who are you, disturbing respectable travellers at this hour?'

'We are seven *devs*,' they all roared together, and banged again with all their might. 'What sort of person are you? Let us see your face.'

So the blind man opened the door a crack and thrust the donkey's face through. He put one of the locusts in the animal's left ear and one into the donkey's right ear. The two locusts bit the donkey's ears with a sudden crunch and the donkey began to roar as if he had been attacked by a lion.

The terrible noise he made rose to the sky and the *devs* sprang back in fright. They scrambled to get away in case they were torn to pieces by the strange animal. So the two brothers spent a happy night there, having taken the locusts out of the donkey's ears and roasted them over a small fire as a snack.

When they woke in the morning, lo and behold, the floor of the room was littered with gems and pieces of gold. The deaf man told the blind man and together they began to collect everything which was of value. They divided it into two heaps, and tied each one into a parcel with their headcloths, then both got onto the donkey's back, one parcel in front of each brother.

'We shall go home rich and become sheikhs with many camels,' said the blind man, shouting in the deaf one's ear.

But his brother was thinking that he might steal the blind man's share as well as having his own, and he was wondering how he could rob his unfortunate brother, so crazed had he become with the newly found riches.

Meanwhile the *devs* were not very far behind, for they dearly loved to eat human flesh and they could follow the donkey's hoof marks on the sandy ground. Soon the deaf man saw them coming in the distance. Quickly, he pulled the blind man off the animal's back, threw the two bundles of treasure into the bushes near the donkey, and started to climb a large tree.

'Quick, brother Wahid,' said Ra'oof. 'Follow me up this tree. The *devs* are almost upon us.' Soon they were both up in the highest branches. But the devs were clever too. They got up on each other's shoulders until together they were almost as high as the tree, and, as they tottered about, the topmost *dev* tried to pull the men from their place of safety.

Seeing their dreadful faces, the deaf brother was terrified, but the blind brother, all unaware of the danger, sat happily on a branch thinking they were safe. Suddenly his brother gave him an accidental shove and he fell right out of the tree onto the head of the topmost *dev*. The donkey began to bray and the deaf brother began to whimper, thinking that any minute Wahid was going to be torn to pieces, but by a happy chance the blind man, being so relaxed, knocked the *devs* to the ground and their bodies broke his fall. The monsters all lay senseless at the foot of the tree but Wahid was uninjured. Down shinned the deaf man and gathered the bundles out of the bushes. Together the brothers galloped off on the donkey as fast as the creature could go.

They rode for a long time till at last they came to the outskirts of their village. Then Wahid said, 'Brother, let me feel my bundle of treasure. It does not seem to be as big as the one you have tied up for yourself.'

'No, no,' shouted the deaf man. 'They are the same size and weight.'

'Oh no, they're not,' said the blind Wahid, getting off the donkey. 'Let me feel your bundle.'

So they came to blows. Ra'oof tried to get hold of some of the blind man's treasure and the bundles broke open, spilling the gems and the gold all around. Sobbing, Wahid gave his brother a colossal whack on the ear, cursing him as he did so. Ra'oof began to shout, saying, 'I can hear you, you wretched fellow, son of a dog. Take that,' and he gave the blind one a thwack on the head.

Wahid shook his head once or twice and then began to jump up and down, shouting gleefully, 'I can see, I can see you and all the treasure and the donkey. Oh bless you, brother. Let us make up and split the treasure equally and go into the village, rich and happy.'

'Praises be to Allah,' cried Ra'oof, gathering up his portion again in his headcloth. 'I can hear. I can hear the barking of the village dogs. Come, let us give the village a feast the like of which they have never had before.'

So they went home together, married the most beautiful girls in the village and lived happily ever after.

The Sultan's Emissary
and the Leopard

NCE UPON A TIME there was a Caliph who was feasting one night with all his courtiers. At the feast was the emissary of the Sultan of Zanzibar, who asked permission of the Caliph to return to his own country the following day.

'By all means, good Zanzibari, go and peace be with you. But do not forget,' said the Caliph graciously, 'to take our gift to your sultan, which goes to him with our most brotherly affection.'

'What gift, most Auspicious One?' asked the emissary, half afraid of what it might be. The Caliph was inclined to practical jokes in rather dubious taste, and he feared that it might have been a giantess or perhaps a pigmy cannibal.

'Why, my most beautiful and well-trained leopard, of course,' laughed the Caliph and clapped his hands for his head huntsman. In came the huntsman with a very elegant leopard on a golden chain, which he presented to the emissary from Zanzibar on the Caliph's instructions.

'May you live forever, O Caliph. A thousand thanks on behalf of my royal master,' said the emissary faintly.

Taking the chain, he led the leopard away to his own chamber. The animal seemed docile enough and was not at all unwilling to be led about by someone who was not its usual keeper. The Zanzibari, whose name was Bilal, prayed to Allah that he could keep the leopard in good humour for the whole journey.

They set out next day and travelled all that day and the next;

the end of the third day found them not far from a wayside inn where people were lodged for the night. Bilal was leading the leopard, feeling very footsore and weary, when he met the keeper of the inn taking his daily stroll.

'Good day, brother,' said Bilal. 'I am looking forward to resting at the inn after my three day's journey with only this leopard for company. Have you a bed ready so that I could settle down and get a good night's sleep before we go on our way again tomorrow?'

'Good friend,' said the innkeeper, 'go ahead and stay in the inn, by all means, but I beg you not to take that leopard, for it will frighten everyone staying here and it might kill the goats and chickens which they are keeping as provisions for their journeys. If you want to have a bed tonight, you will have to dispose of the leopard at once.'

'But this magnificent animal is a present from the Caliph to my master, the Sultan of Zanzibar!' cried Bilal. 'I cannot dispose of it as you say. If the Caliph sends my master a letter asking how his leopard fares and I have killed it instead of presenting it to His Excellency; why, he would strike my head from my shoulders without even asking what had happened.'

'I see,' nodded the innkeeper. 'But I cannot have the animal near my lodgers. However, to save you sleeping out in the open and being exposed to the dangers of wolves or thieves tonight, you may sleep in a small house which I own just outside the town. Unfortunately the house is inhabited by an evil *jinn* which gives those who live in it no peace. It is forever rattling chains and moaning or screeching, breaking china and moving furniture about, which makes it impossible to live there. If you stay there you must take no notice of the *jinn*, and I dare say it will take no notice of the leopard.'

Bilal thanked the man and was directed to the house.

'Perhaps the *jinn* will not be at home tonight,' thought he, leading the leopard up to the door and lifting the latch. Inside the house, which was clean and swept, there were a few plates and dishes lying broken on the table. However, Bilal was so tired that he lay down on the bed and let the leopard leap up onto the quilt beside him. He hooked the chain over one of the bed-posts and soon both were fast asleep.

Just as the moon rose and the owls began to hoot, the door of the house opened and the *jinn* appeared. Howling with laughter and making the floor shake with his huge feet, the *jinn* began to eat a goat which he had skinned. All this activity caused Bilal to wake up. He looked on in horror as the *jinn*, which was venomously ugly with a face like a demon and teeth protruding like fangs, chewed pieces of the goat, tearing at the flesh with long talons. Bilal could scarcely believe his eyes as he watched the creature.

Suddenly the leopard awoke and leapt from the bed, its golden chain rattling and its eyes blazing with rage.

'Ha, ha, ha,' said the *jinn*. 'What is this spotted cat doing here?'

The leopard, which had been so quiet and well-mannered all the time it had been travelling with the emissary, now began to snarl, showing its teeth in a terrifying way. Then a fierce battle began.

Bilal watched with horror as, this way and that, amid tables and stools, pots and pans, the *jinn* and the leopard bit and clawed each other with the most fearsome growls and grunts. One minute the *jinn* would be on top, then the leopard, but soon it was obvious that the *jinn* was getting the worst of it. Peeping out of the cupboard where he had hidden at the height of the fray, Bilal saw the leopard, with one last fierce swipe of its paw, strike such a blow that the *jinn* went howling up the chimney and out of sight.

'My brave leopard, you are indeed a good friend,' cried Bilal, leading the now purring animal back to bed, where both lay down and slept the rest of the night in peace.

Early next morning the innkeeper was at the door with some bread and milk, wondering how things had gone in the night.

'Brother, thank you for the shelter of this pleasant house. The blessings of Allah be upon you,' said Bilal as he shared the milk with the leopard, who was contentedly washing its face and paws in the sunshine.

'But, but, what about the *jinn*?' cried the astonished innkeeper. 'Was there no sight of the evil creature last night?'

'Certainly, brother,' responded the emissary airily, 'but this excellent leopard soon got rid of that demon. There was a wonderful fight and the *jinn* escaped up the chimney. I doubt if you will be worried by it again.'

'A thousand thanks to you,' said the other. 'Take the rest of these provisions for the next stage of your journey and may Allah lengthen your days.'

With the man's heartfelt blessings ringing in his ears, Bilal took the leopard's golden chain and set off along the road. That night they reached some caves and sheltered there when darkness fell, huddling together for warmth. No sooner had midnight come than Bilal awoke and saw the horrible figure of the *jinn* at the cave entrance.

'Human being,' bellowed the *jinn*. 'I have tracked you down by the power invested in me by Suleiman, son of David, upon whom be peace. Come outside so that I may devour you as a punishment, for your great spotted cat drove me out of a very comfortable house which I much enjoyed.'

As the *jinn* finished speaking, the leopard awoke with a start and Bilal could not hold on to the chain. So he let it go and saw the leopard leap upon the *jinn* as if it were nothing but a piece of old leather, shaking it as a dog shakes a rag. Howling with pain, the *jinn* ran away, while the leopard, purring with pleasure, came back to lie against Bilal's side in the cave.

'Oh my brave animal, how shall I thank you?' said Bilal, and soon they were both asleep.

Next day they set off again, and at last they arrived at the spice-scented island of Zanzibar. As the boat arrived at the jetty, all the onlookers cheered at the sight of the emissary with the beautiful docile leopard on its golden chain. Bilal, returning home after so long in a foreign land, wept to see his own countrymen again, and though he was sorry to part with the leopard, he took it to the court to give to the Sultan.

When the nobles saw the animal they shrank back, and one or two took to their heels, but the leopard merely padded along beside Bilal, looking at them with its golden eyes.

'Oh, great Sultan,' cried Bilal, prostrating himself before the throne. 'Here from the Caliph of a thousand suns comes a rare leopard as a present to your Augustness.'

'What?' bellowed the Sultan, twirling his moustache. 'A leopard? A wild creature like that as a pet? No! While you have been gone, the King of the Ethiopians has sent me two lions which are on excellent terms with each other, to be my body-guards. If I were to introduce this fierce looking leopard into the court, the fur would certainly begin to fly.'

At his words, there entered two fine young lions, each with two black boys holding them on a chain. The leopard's tail began to swish and its eyes grew to glistening orbs. Bilal found that he had to use all his strength to pull the animal back, for it was beginning to growl with rage at the sight of the lions.

'Bilal, take the leopard as a gift, with my thanks for your task well done in the country of the Caliph,' said the Sultan hastily. 'But get that animal out of here. Take it with my blessing, for it would be one cat too many among the mice at my court.'

Breathlessly, Bilal hurried the leopard away and returned to his own house. Bathed and changed, he lay on his divan and the servants brought him spiced rice with meatballs to eat. At his feet, looking at him with love and devotion, sat the beautiful spotted leopard, now at peace with all the world.

'Dearest leopard,' said Bilal happily, drying his hand on a napkin after the servant had cleared away the meal, 'Allah be praised that our Honourable Sultan has seen fit to give you to me, for after our adventures together I could wish for no better companion than you.'

'Oh, excellent master,' cried the leopard, 'it rejoices my heart to hear your words, for they will set me free from my bondage. Know, O Worthy Bilal, that I am no leopard but a princess who was bewitched by a wicked magician when I was seventeen, in my father's house in far-away Tashkand. Say that you are free and willing to marry me and I shall turn into a woman again before your very eyes.'

'Bless my soul,' cried Bilal. 'Am I hearing right? Why, of course I am free and willing to marry you and release you from the spell — we shall celebrate our wedding this very night.'

At his words, the leopard changed into a beautiful young woman with long black hair, almond-shaped eyes and a gown made of spotted silk which came to her ankles. Around her waist was a belt studded with precious stones and on her head a jewelled cap. Bilal was smitten with love for her on the spot and they were married in great joy. Allah sent them many sons, and Bilal and the Princess of Tashkand lived happily until the end of their days.

The Faithful Gazelle

ONCE UPON A TIME there was a poor beggar called Mustafa who slept on the outside oven of a rich man's kitchen. One morning he was awakened by the cries of a salesman, who was shouting, 'Gazelles, gazelles, buy my fine gazelles!'

The beggar said, 'There is no one awake at this hour in the rich man's house. Cease making your noise until a more civilised hour, brother.'

The gazelle seller, who had several of the poor creatures in a cage on top of a donkey cart, replied, 'Would you like to buy one of these fine gazelles?'

'I have only a handful of coppers,' said the beggar. 'What would I do with a gazelle anyway?' But he climbed down off the oven to talk to the gazelle seller.

At that moment, one of the small animals poked its head out of the cage and said in a low voice to the beggar, 'Buy me and you will not be sorry.'

Mustafa was so astonished that he said to the salesman, 'Here is all I have in the world — three copper coins. Is it enough to buy this gazelle with its head out of the cage?'

'Take it and be blessed,' cried the man, and released the gazelle. 'I will let it go for whatever you can give me. I should only have to feed the thing.' He closed the cage again, took the three coppers from Mustafa, and went on his way to the nearest tea house.

'Well,' said Mustafa to the gazelle, 'what now? I have bought you and now I have nothing left in the world until I can get something more by begging on the steps of the mosque at the time of the midday prayer.'

'You will not regret buying me,' said the gazelle, 'for I shall make your fortune.'

'How is that?' cried Mustafa, 'and what should I do next?'

'Do nothing. Simply stay here till I return,' said the gazelle, and it trotted away.

The tattered beggar scratched his head. He would probably never see the wretched animal again, he thought. How had he allowed himself to be so deluded as to give three copper coins for a talking gazelle? Probably the creature was bewitched and would bring him bad luck. Ruminating thus, he sat down again on the oven to wait until the rich man's servants woke. Perhaps they would throw out some food that he could eat.

Meanwhile the gazelle ran on until it reached the house of a noble prince. It bowed to him and said, 'O Prince of a thousand blessings, I am the slave of a great and noble merchant whose caravan has just been attacked and plundered by thieves. Could you please send some clothes for him to put on, so that he does not have to appear before you completely naked when he comes to pay you a visit?'

'Certainly, good gazelle,' said the hospitable prince. 'My servants shall give you a white linen shirt and a robe of the finest wool to take to your master. When he has recovered from his shock, let him come here to my house so that I may cause a sheep to be roasted in his honour.'

The gazelle thanked the prince and said, 'I was to bring you this emerald in payment for any clothes which you might send, as my master does not wish to accept your kindness for nothing.' Thereupon the gazelle placed a flawless emerald at the feet of the prince and bounded away with the clothes upon its back. The prince was delighted with the value of the gift, and resolved that if the man did appear he would offer him the hand of his daughter, for he was apparently a man of much substance.

The gazelle went back to Mustafa and said, 'Look, I have brought you these clothes from a rich prince. Cast off your rags, bathe in the river and put on these magnificent garments.'

The beggar was amazed and said, 'How in the world did you manage to do this? Never in my life have I seen such beautiful clothes.'

'Do as I tell you,' said the gazelle, 'and I shall get you a rich wife as well. Did you not give me back my liberty by buying me from the man who had put me in a cage?'

The long and the short of it was that the clothes transformed the beggar into a man who could sit in a royal court without shame.

'Now, follow me,' said the gazelle, and it trotted off into a ruined building. 'Look under the third brick on the left and you will see a treasure.'

Sure enough, as Mustafa lifted the brick, he saw the gleam of gold and precious stones in a cavity below. Joyfully, he filled his pockets and his money belt until he had as much as he could carry. 'What a piece of luck!' cried the beggar. 'I shall never have to go without anything for the rest of my days.'

'Not if you marry into the family of the prince,' said the gazelle. 'Buy yourself a horse and some boots, and we shall set out for the noble prince's house at once.'

An hour later Mustafa, mounted on a beautiful white horse, followed the gazelle as it sped along before him. Soon they reached a tall house with many balconies surrounded by a beautiful garden.

'Wait here,' said the gazelle, 'until I come for you. And remember that you are now a rich merchant whose caravan has been set upon by thieves and plundered.'

'I understand,' said Mustafa. 'I shall stay here until you return.'

The gazelle then went back into the inner courtyard of the house and, presenting himself to the prince, let fall a priceless ruby at his feet.

'My master, the noble Mustafa, sends you blessings and peace and requests that he may call upon you at once to thank you for the clothes that you sent him after his recent misfortune. In the meantime, here is a small token of his regard which he wishes to give you as a mark of his respect.'

'Excellent gazelle,' cried the prince, 'let your master hasten here as fast as he can, for I am eager to meet him and he should start thinking of himself as my son-in-law from this moment.'

The gazelle returned to Mustafa and acquainted him with what the prince had said. Soon the one-time beggar and the rich and venerable prince were sitting together, drinking tea like old friends. By nightfall, when a sheep had been roasted and eaten, the prince came to the delicate subject of his daughter.

'My son,' said he, placing his hand on Mustafa's arm, 'I'm glad that I have kept my daughter until you came, for I can think of no more suitable match for her. I shall arrange for the marriage rites to be solemnised tomorrow and she shall come to you with her servants and her dowry all complete.' The one-time beggar was delighted at this news and thanked his lucky stars for bringing him such good fortune.

The next day at the wedding he was congratulated by every member of the family, each of whom piled gifts before the happy pair. The bridal feast went on for hours, till at last they were led to a bedroom hung with rare carpets and decorated with lamps of burnished brass set with coral. While they slept, the gazelle lay across the threshold keeping watch.

The months passed. The prince had to go on a journey, so he gave his daughter and new son-in-law the grand house to live in until his return. There were tinkling fountains in blue-tiled courtyards, carved wooden balconies and vast rooms with painted pillars. Mustafa became more and more conceited and forgot completely what he owed to the gazelle. He spent all day playing backgammon with his friends.

One day the gazelle went to his mistress and said, 'Lady, ask my master if he would give me a bowl of curds and honey prepared with his own hands, for I am feeling ill and fear that I may die.'

So the girl went to her husband and said, 'Peace and blessings upon you, husband. Please give the gazelle a bowl of curds and honey prepared with your own hands, as it is ill and fears that it may die.'

And the man answered, 'Foolish one, do not worry about the animal. Did I not buy it for a few copper coins? Take no notice and leave me to my game of backgammon.'

The girl went back to the gazelle, which was lying on the ground looking very weak and thin. She said, 'I cannot get your master to come. Shall I prepare you the mixture so that you will get better?'

The gazelle said, 'No, mistress, thank you. I would rather that my master did it. Please go back to him and beg him for my sake to do as I ask, or I shall die.'

So she ran back to Mustafa and said, 'Come quickly. The gazelle begs you to do as it asks, or indeed it will die, for it is now so weak and thin and is lying on the ground.'

But again her husband would not do anything and told her to go to the gazelle and give it a bowl of milk herself. When the girl got back to where the gazelle was lying, she saw that its eyes were very dull, and when she had told it that Mustafa was not coming, it dropped its head and died.

That night, lying in his luxurious bedroom, the man who had been a beggar said to his wife, 'What happened to the gazelle? You did not come back to tell me.'

She answered sadly, 'It died, and I am so grieved at the way you disregarded the poor creature's plea that I have decided that when my father comes back, I shall take my dowry and return to my family, for I no longer love you.'

'Foolish woman,' cried Mustafa, 'go to sleep and in the morning you will have forgotten all about this matter.' Within a few moments he was snoring.

In the middle of the night he had a dream. He thought he saw the gazelle again and its eyes were very sad. 'Why did you not bring me a bowl of curds and honey when I begged you to do so? Had you forgotten that you owed all your good fortune to me? I was grateful because you bought my liberty back for me. Why could you not show me one act of kindness when I was in need?'

'I asked my wife to take you a bowl of milk,' cried Mustafa feeling very ashamed of himself. 'It was not the same thing,' said the gazelle, and it disappeared.

In a great fright Mustafa sat up and found he was Mustafa the beggar again, dressed in tatters, sitting against the oven of a rich man's house in the moonlight, and he remained a beggar for the rest of his days.

❦ TALES FROM INDIA ❦

The Story of the Taj Mahal

*S*HAH JAHAN, KING OF THE WORLD, ruled the vast Mughal empire in the fifteenth century. He was a man of many gifts, of rare artistic talent, and one who loved, above all human things, his wife Mumtaz Mahal.

She was beautiful and talented in the art of music and story telling, and like the famous Sheherazade, told her lord many a tale to pass away the anxious hours when Shah Jahan was awaiting news from distant outposts. The queen was pictured in many miniatures with a canopy of pearls hanging from a golden crown or partially veiled in enchanting draperies, so that only her long, expressive almond-shaped eyes were visible above a mouth of delicate coral, her neck encircled with row upon row of emeralds and yet more pearls.

The Emperor Shah Jahan was a man of many moods and is reputed to have been a most difficult man to live with. No one ever understood him as well as did Mumtaz Mahal, his favourite wife and the light of his palace, and it is said that because the queen was seven women, one for each day of the week, he never tired of her. When she died, the emperor roared at the physician who brought the sad news to him, 'Dead? What do you mean by that, you fool?'

With bent head, the physician answered, 'There is but one meaning to that word, Sire.'

And Shah Jahan, King of the World, leaned his face against his arm and sobbed like a child. When the emperor had recovered his outward composure, he was still heart-broken at his wife's death. Nothing could console him except that a tomb shaped like a white mosque be built for her that would be worthy of her name. It did not matter to Shah Jahan that it might take the whole of his life, as long as it was the most beautiful monument ever erected to a woman in the whole world

Craftsmen and builders, calligraphers and workers in marble were gathered from established art centres in India, Iran and Central Asia. It is believed that workers in marble were even summoned from Italy. The Taj Mahal harmoniously combined the great building traditions of Central Asia, Iran and India, all of which placed tremendous emphasis on the beauty of geometric design within a building.

Shah Jahan watched from his window as the white tomb of Mumtaz Mahal was slowly erected, as near to perfection as anything made by human hands. 'When I die,' he said, 'I shall be buried on the other side of the River Jumna in a tomb of similar size and workmanship, except that it will be constructed of black marble to show that I was only the shadow of Mumtaz Mahal. Without her, I have no reality. Remember this which I have said.'

Year by year the wondrous edifice grew in size, but Shah Jahan was never to see even the beginning of his own black marble tomb on the banks of the Jumna, for his son, the rebellious Prince Aurangzeb, overthrew his father and imprisoned him.

'I care not where you put me except that from one of my windows I must be able to see the building of the Taj Mahal,' said Shah Jahan. And so until he died, Shah Jahan continued to watch it being built.

The Taj Mahal appears translucent, as if it were made of mother-of-pearl, though in fact it has rich polychrome decoration inset in the white marble. It appears almost to float on a tank of water, like a group of Indian lilies floating on the black water of their pond. This beautiful building, one of the wonders of the world today, emphasises immortality and regeneration, the victory of life over death. It stands as a perfect example of Mughal architecture and the world's greatest symbol of a husband's love for his wife.

In an underground chamber beneath the Taj Mahal are two simple marble tombs where Shah Jahan, King of the World, and Mumtaz Mahal, light of the palace, lie together in perfect peace. It is a rare place to visit and stirs the heart of even the most hardened tourist, commemorating a King's heartbreak and his true concern that Mumtaz Mahal should always be remembered in this poem in marble. It is, in fact, a tribute to them both.

The Man who Made Gold

ONCE UPON A TIME there lived a man whose sole ambition was to make gold. He had read that it could be done and had been done, but how it was to be done was another matter. So he set himself up as an alchemist with a furnace that belched forth flames when he worked the bellows strongly enough, and shelves full of bottles containing all sorts of liquids and crystals, and magical things like dried crocodile legs and snakes pickled in brine as well.

People came to him from near and far to get his remedies for the palsy, the toothache and being possessed of devils in one's knees or elbows, so he made quite enough money to keep himself comfortably even if he never discovered how to make gold. But he was greedy and determined, so he went on experimenting in every spare moment that he had. Every night, when he was sure that his wife was asleep, he used to go downstairs and read every recipe in all the ancient books that had ever been written on the subject.

In one it was suggested that, in order to make gold, he should use the juice of a certain very rare wild flower, so he spent many hours in the early dawn looking for it. When he did find the flower and added it to his crucible that night, he thought that he had succeeded. The ingot came out of the fire, bright and gleaming like gold. Next morning however, when he went down to the cellar to see if his gold was still there, he was disappointed to see that it had apparently only been gold for a few hours and now it was once more as grey as lead.

One day, his wife brought the baby son to him and said, 'Will you please hold him for a few minutes? I have to go out to get some meat — the maid-servant didn't come this morning and we need food for the midday meal.'

So the alchemist took the baby and wandered about carrying it, not quite thinking about what he was doing, while he continued with his experiments. His wife could only have been gone for half an hour and he was stirring the liquid in a great vat with a steel rod, faster and faster, when suddenly — he didn't really know how it happened — he dropped his son in.

There wasn't even a sound from the baby, and when he fished it out he was amazed to find that it had turned into pure gold. The mixture in the vat was the right one at last! He had great difficulty in lifting the baby out for it was so heavy. He was quite out of breath by the time he had carried it to the table. It was solid gold of the finest colour he had ever seen.

'It must be priceless, priceless!' he shouted. 'I have made gold! I have actually made gold at last!'

As he spoke this aloud, the magnitude of his discovery came to him, and he began to dance about the room like a man demented. What a miracle! What a boon to mankind! All he had to do was to drop something into the liquid and he could turn it to gold.

At that moment the cat dashed into the room hotly pursued by the dog. He picked up the cat and threw it into the liquid, and hey presto! — in a few minutes a golden cat was sitting beside the golden baby on the table with a golden mouse between its teeth. The dog began jumping up and worrying the alchemist and pulling at his long sleeves, seeking some attention. The alchemist picked up the dog and walked towards the vat. Somehow, he didn't know how, the dog fell from his hands right into the greeny grey liquid in the vat.

'Oh, good heavens,' said the delighted alchemist, 'it's happened again! Pure, solid gold!'

It was not a very big dog and it took its place, still dripping wet, beside the baby and the cat.

'In time, I shall be able to buy the whole world, ' murmured the happy man to himself, stroking his long and straggly beard with trembling fingers. 'When my dear wife comes in, I can show her that I've at last been successful.'

Then his smile faded as he realised that his wife might be very angry indeed to find their baby turned into a golden statuette, let alone both the cat and the dog of which she was also extremely fond.

'What am I going to do?' he whispered, rubbing his hands over the fabulous golden treasure before him. 'This is really going to need a bit of explaining, and even when I have explained, will Fatima be as pleased as I am?'

He had to admit to himself that the answer must definitely be no. Just at that moment his wife, a small, shrewish woman, came back and began to shout to him to bring the baby to her upstairs.

'Are you deaf, husband?' she shrilled. 'Can't you hear me?'

He called out, 'All right, my dear, I can hear you. Would you, um, er, kindly come down here a minute? I have something really quite wonderful to show you.'

Throwing down her basket, Fatima came down the stairs quickly. In her bad-tempered haste, her new slippers slipped on the damp stone, taking her feet from under her, and *flop*! she was right in the vat before you could count to three. The alchemist peered in and there was his small wife turned completely into gold, her golden fingers reaching out to him like the claws of a bird.

'Merciful heavens,' cried the excited alchemist. 'I have got a really wonderful amount of gold here. I shall build myself a grand house. I shall get myself another wife, young and beautiful this time. All I have to do now is get the Fatima statue out of the vat.'

He pulled with all his might but she would not budge. He fixed up a pulley but the weight of his golden wife was almost too much for the thick ropes. He pulled on them with might and main and being immensely strong, he at last managed to get the vast piece of gold onto the floor.

The liquid in the vat was giving off a strange and quite intoxicating odour. He leaned on the edge of the vat, trying to get his breath. The last hour's hauling and lifting had started to take its toll of his strength. He leaned against the vat and looked down into the liquid which was bubbling as if it were about to boil. Whatever could be the matter? He leaned further forward and suddenly it seemed as if something was pushing him into the vat. He gave a great shout, but nobody heard.

His wife's golden statue had toppled forward and nudged him into the liquid. Within a few seconds, the alchemist himself was turned into pure, solid gold. The cellar door banged shut and jammed itself tightly closed.

It was a long time before anyone found out that the alchemist's house was empty. Then it was locked up by the watchman who patrolled the streets at night in case the alchemist came back, for it looked as if he had gone somewhere in a hurry. But when the house began to fall down, the authorities gave orders that it should be demolished before it became a danger to the public. In the cellar, buried by debris, were all the golden figures looking as if they had been there for the past hundred years at least. So the pure gold statues of a man, a woman, a baby, a cat and a dog went to swell the treasury of the King. The items were placed in the care of the royal treasurer as objects in need of protection, being antiques from a bygone age. They remain there, in the treasury, to this day.

The Young Ant

ONCE UPON A TIME, in a city completely populated by ants, there was a young ant who had been given a very fine education. No money had been spared to equip him with the finest brain an ant could ever have and he felt very pleased with himself.

One day a great shadow fell over the ant city, completely obscuring the light of the sun. 'It's our oldest enemy! Get away, run, hide, flee for your lives!' cried all the wise old ants through loud-speakers in all corners of the city. 'No time to say more. Just flee!'

'Whatever can this be about?' questioned the young ant. 'If there is something which endangers us, surely we can all get together and talk it over rationally. I, with the benefit of my very good education, will stay behind and argue with whatever this enemy might be. I will suggest that we take time and reach a compromise. We are rational ants. I think anyone in their right mind ought to agree.'

As he was finishing this thought, the long tongue of the anteater came out and swallowed him up.

And the wise old man who told me this story said, 'If you feel you are qualified to argue a point, be sure that you know your adversary as well.'

The Miser and the Generous Man

ONCE UPON A TIME in the land of India there lived two men who decided to travel together to the city of Delhi, to see the sights. One was a very kind-hearted and generous man and the other was a tight-fisted miser.

During the journey, whenever it was time to pay for tea or food, it was always the generous man who opened his purse. Whenever there was a beggar needing a coin, it was he who gave alms. The miserly man always waited till the things were paid for or the beggar had gone before he went for his purse, but he never opened it. He lived completely on the kindness of the generous man, who never even noticed it.

As they walked towards Delhi, it came about that all the generous man's food, water and money were dissipated. When they sat down together under a tree to get some shade, the generous man said, 'Well, I'm afraid my things are all finished. Could you please let me have a drink of water from your water bottle?'

'No, I'm not going to share my provisions and money with you,' cried the miser. 'More fool you if you have let it all be frittered away — always throwing your money and your water about. You let at least three old beggars swig from your water bottle. Not likely — I'm keeping all I've got for myself.'

He pushed aside the generous man's hand, which reaching out for the water, but he took a long drink himself. Then he jumped up and ran off, leaving the unfortunate generous man in a dreadful state of thirst. There was no food or water so the poor fellow picked a few blades of grass and began to chew them. Now, strange as it may seem, the grass under that very tree had the magical property of being able to give any human who ate it the power to understand the language of animals. So while he was lying there and trying to get his strength back, the generous man with blades of grass between his teeth saw two mongooses playing with a dead snake.

'Oh, brother,' said one mongoose to the other, 'look at that stupid fellow lying there with nothing to eat or drink while the well is no more than five minutes walk up the road. Really, these humans don't deserve to live in the same world as us, do they?'

Scarcely daring to believe his ears, or that what the animal was saying might be true, the generous man hurried up the road, buoyed up by fresh hope, and sure enough, he found the well. After a deep, refreshing drink and having refilled his water bottle, the man set off along the long road to Delhi, his hopes restored.

Soon he arrived at the tomb of a saint which was being looked after by a keeper. He was given something to eat and sent further upon his way. Now the miser had also stopped at the tomb and been given a meal as soon as he arrived. But seeing the donations that believers had left for the upkeep of the place, the miser had waited until the old man was asleep and then stolen the money from its copper bowl. Then he escaped upon the old man's donkey.

Meanwhile, the generous man was resting beneath a tree beside a wall as he continued on his way to Delhi. Two owls came and perched on the topmost branch of the tree. The generous man heard one bird say, 'Where did you get that gold coin you have in your beak? I haven't seen you with a thing like that before.'

'Oh yes, my friend,' said the other. 'There is something interesting which I meant to tell you about. A mole which has a hole very near this tree has just come upon a buried treasure which must have been the fortune of at least a hundred Nawabs. You know how very short-sighted moles are, so it is quite easy to carry off a great deal of the hoard from under its nose.' The owl hooted with laughter and thus dropped the coin it was holding in its beak.

The generous man saw that it was real red gold. He looked around until he found the mole's burrow and dug up enough gold to fill his satchel. Then he went on his way.

At last he arrived and bought himself new clothes immediately, as his own were quite worn out and not suitable for a town like Delhi. Then he took a room in a lodging house and began to enjoy himself again. He had forgotten all about the wretched miser's behaviour and, meeting others like himself, started behaving generously again, giving away a lot of his gold to all those who might be in need.

As news of his behaviour spread and began to be discussed all over Delhi, it soon got to the ears of the miser, who was living in a mean hovel not far away. So he went to the King of Delhi to complain, saying, 'Most auspicious Monarch, most illustrious King, I was robbed by a man from my home town with whom I was travelling some time ago, and I hear that he is now in the city throwing my money about. I beg that justice be done and that he is flung into prison and that my possessions are returned to me. Live forever, O King, and hear my plea.'

So the generous man found himself seized by ungentle hands and thrown into prison. 'What has happened?' he wanted to know. 'What is to become of me?'

'You know full well what is the matter, you thief!' shouted the jailer. 'You'll be thrown to the vultures after you've been hanged tomorrow.'

The unfortunate generous man tried to tell his side of the story, but no one would listen. That night, as he lay in his dungeon in the darkness, he shivered as he heard the rats come out and start scrabbling in the corner among the bones thrown there by previous occupants. Two rats began squeaking to each other, and after a few moments the generous man realised that he could understand what they were saying:

'Did you hear the news today?' one rat asked. 'What a pity that it should happen to the King's daughter. She's the most beautiful creature in the whole kingdom.'

'Why, what has happened to her?' asked the second rat. 'I have never seen her myself as we do not often have a chance to get into the palace. But you know how it is.'

'Well,' said the first rat, 'I heard that she has gone blind and that all the court physicians, be they ever so learned, cannot find out how to restore her sight.'

'Can it be restored?' asked the second rat as it gnawed away at the bones. 'Surely there must be some way. You can imagine how grateful the King would be. He might open up all the prisons and let out the prisoners in gratitude,' and the rats laughed noisily.

'Well,' said the first rat, 'there is a way of curing her and I happen to know it. Old Haji Mulla, who has got that large black goat in the small courtyard near the Blue Mosque, has the antidote to what ails the Princess. If someone could clip the hairs from the tail of that old black goat, burn them over charcoal and rub the ashes on the Princess' eyelids, then it is certain that she would be able to see again.'

As soon as the generous man heard this he began banging on the door of his prison, and he banged and kicked until the jailer came.

'Let me out. I am a physician,' he shouted. 'I can make the Princess see again. I must see the King. Let me out and I'll show you it is the truth.'

The noise was so loud that the King asked what was going on down below.

'Sire, it is but one of the rogues trying to call attention to himself,' said the Grand Vizier after finding out the cause of the tumult. 'He says he can make the Princess see again because of some special medicine only he knows about.'

'Bring him here at once,' ordered the King, and the generous man was hauled into the throne room and thrown down in front of him.

'So,' said his Majesty, 'now you're here, what can you do for my daughter's blindness? Do it you must, or you will be very severely dealt with if your claim has no truth in it.'

'It is perfectly true, your Majesty,' said the generous man. 'Just let me go and get the ingredients and I will restore the Princess's sight at once.'

In less time than it takes to tell, the generous man had got the hairs from the tail of old Haji Mulla's black goat, burnt them over the charcoal burner and held the ashes in his hand ready to rub on the blind Princess's eyelids. The whole court was in attendance as the delicate operation was performed. The Princess lay stretched out on a divan and the generous man leaned over her.

He rubbed a small amount of grey ash onto the Princess's eyelids and within two minutes she opened her eyes. 'I can see, I can see,' she cried joyfully, and all the courtiers in their rainbow-coloured robes began dancing for joy.

'Well, veil yourself instantly,' the King said to her and, demurely, the Princess obeyed. The King's joy knew no bounds, and the generous man received all his gold back from the rascally miser. Not only that, but the Princess had fallen in love with her healer the moment her eyes were opened, so the King gave the generous man the hand of the beautiful Princess in marriage.

And they had a long and happy life, for no one is a better husband than a kind and generous man.

The Story of the Koh-i-Noor

THIS IS THE STORY OF THE KOH-I-NOOR, that fabulous diamond, the name of which means Mountain of Light in Persian. At present, it is in the crown of the Queen of England and it is unlikely to be worn by any male ruler for the time being, at least. It has been said from its earliest days that it will bring ill luck unless it is worn by a woman.

When it was first discovered, it was cut carefully in the old oriental style and weighed much more than it does now, as it has since been faceted in the western tradition of diamond cutting. Originally it was in the possession of Nadir Shah Durani, the King of Afghanistan who first united the kingdom. Later, Shah Shuja, Emir of Afghanistan, kept it securely concealed in his turban within the folds bound close to his head and hidden from covetous eyes, for it already had a history of murder and intrigue. More than one life had been lost in the struggle for possession of it.

Each time the stone changed hands it was re-cut to the owner's wishes, and finally it was cut so that it glittered as no other diamond had done before.

Now Ranjit Singh, Maharaja of Kashmir, was playing chess one night with Shah Shuja who owned the stone, and the Emir was admiring the string of priceless pearls worth a King's ransom, which Ranjit Singh wore round his neck. But even as he spoke he congratulated himself upon the hiding place of his own jewel, the finest in the known world, the blessed Mountain of Light, the light of his life.

Now Ranjit Singh had heard of the Koh-i-Noor, for who

indeed had not? It had come to his ears from the lips of a highly placed, well-bribed spy that the priceless diamond was hidden in the folds of Shah Shuja's turban. A scheme had formed in his wily mind and he put the plan into action.

It was a hot night and the palace fans were scarcely able to keep the brows of the two royal chess players cool. Iced drinks were brought with fresh ice made from the everlasting snows of the Hindu Kush, and the Maharaja congratulated the Emir on his success in bringing the ice from his mountains. They sipped the drinks made from the crushed ice, sweetened with sugar cane and the juice of the blood-red pomegranates of Jalalabad.

The game was going well. The two men were superbly matched and the musicians and dancing girls in the courtyard below were some of the finest of all Hindustan, for they had come with the Maharaja. With one final move, the Emir declared checkmate, and with a polite smile indicated that they should retire to the banqueting hall. Ranjit Singh also smiled and followed his royal host to the silken cushions where they were to partake of a truly sumptuous repast. Each dish was more delicious than the last, and the conversation between the Maharaja of Kashmir and Shah Shuja became increasingly warm. Indeed the stiffness of court protocol and the veneer of political politeness seemed to have been stripped away, and the two rulers appeared to be as dear to each other as if they had been twin brothers.

At last the meal was at an end, the entertainment was over and it was time for the Maharaja to leave. Shah Shuja was just taking his powerful guest to the door of the palace, thinking to himself that the evening had passed with less trouble than he might have imagined, when the Maharaja bowed to Shah Shuja and said with his hand upon his heart:

'Most auspicious ruler, most worthy Emir, dear friend and brother, although I have not had the pleasure of knowing you all my life, I now truly feel as if I had. In order to cement this happy relationship and for the betterment of our future friendship and regard, let us now exchange turbans, which, as you know, is the highest honour possible.' And he took from his perfectly formed, almost bald cranium the turban trimmed with silk which Shah Shuja had been viewing all evening as a concoction in the worst possible taste.

With a sinking heart the Emir valiantly took off his own white cotton turban, as plain as a pale jasmine bud, and handed it over to the Maharaja of Kashmir. To have refused such an honour would have been to commit a dreadful political blunder, for to arouse the anger of so powerful a ruler as Ranjit Singh would indeed court disaster. Bravely, Shah Shuja gave up his turban with the Koh-i-Noor concealed in it and it is said that from that time forward he never smiled again.

So the Koh-i-Noor, the Mountain of Light, passed out of the Afghan court and when Ranjit Singh himself lost his life, somehow it got into the hands of the British Ambassador, who saw that it was speedily sent to England, where it became one of the most brilliant of the crown jewels.

Queen Mary wore it at her coronation and in India at the Grand Durbar; now it shines in the Jewel House of the Tower of London where it is likely to remain. Had it not been for that exchange of turbans, who knows where it might be today?

The King who Had Everything

ONCE UPON A TIME there was a King of Hindustan who was both happy and beloved of his people. He was handsome and well skilled in all the arts; his palace gardens were beautiful and full of roses; the horses in the royal stables were the finest in the land; his treasury was full of jewels and gold. He had everything.

His father, when he was about to die, had said, 'My son, soon you shall be King, so let me give you something which is a great heirloom in our family. Read it and you will learn much', and he had handed the young Prince a very old book written by hand, with letters illuminated in gold — and then he had died.

But though he often meant to read the book, the new King never got the opportunity. The Viziers of the court made him appear at one great feast after the other, then came his coronation which lasted many days, and after that there was his wedding to the Princess Fatima, and yet more feasting. Then there were hunting parties and visits to the boundaries of his dominions — there never seemed to be any time to read.

It was only when his own son was seventeen years old that the King realised that he had not yet read the ancient book. He had everything — rich and powerful neighbours who were friendly, jewels and treasure in his vaults — and yet he had no time to read. One afternoon he decided that he must obey his father's last wish. He was just going to his private study when the Chief Vizier came and bowed low before him.

'Oh, glorious King,' said the Vizier, 'see these beautiful opals which have been sent as presents by the Emir of…'

'I'm going to read,' said the King, frowning.

'Read, your Majesty? Read?' said the Vizier. 'Have I not this day chosen two new storytellers for your Majesty's pleasure?'

'See this wonderful velvet for the new state robes,' chimed in the royal robe-maker, pushing his way to the front. 'The Queen and the Princesses have been delighted with the colours.'

The King said more firmly, 'I wish to read and I do not want to be disturbed.'

In his study, he opened the secret drawer in which the manuscript lay wrapped in a piece of silk. He began to read the book. The first page had the following words upon it, 'He who has everything, sometimes has nothing.' The King read on. After an hour, he wrapped the book up again in the green silk and made his way to the harem.

'My Queen,' he said to the royal lady, 'give me leave to speak without comment for the next few minutes.'

The Queen bowed her head.

'I shall have to go away,' said he, 'for though I am King of all Hindustan I am not a wise enough man. I am seeking knowledge which I shall never find here surrounded by all this luxury. I am going on a journey. If I find what will satisfy me, I shall return. If I do not, you must not grieve, I beg you. Put our eldest son on the throne and guide him yourself.'

Then he dressed himself in a robe such as travelling dervishes or holy men wear and he set off with a staff and a few coins in his pocket. The ancient book, wrapped in green silk, was under his arm.

Years passed and, when it seemed that the King was not returning, the young Prince was put upon the throne.

One day, an old traveller in a simple robe such as dervishes wear was washing his hands at the fountain of the Friday Mosque and said to a townsman, 'What sort of man is the King?'

'Why, his Majesty is the most handsome and cultivated person in the whole of our land,' was the reply. 'His treasure house is full of wonders, his horses are magnificent, the roses of the royal garden are world famous. He has everything.'

'Then,' said the traveller, 'I charge you to give him this. It is a valuable book which I have had in trust for him for many years. Give it to him and here is a coin for your trouble.'

The townsman agreed, and the old man made his way out of the gate on the back of the last donkey in a departing caravan. At the palace, having gained the royal presence, the honest towns-man placed at the feet of the young King a small book wrapped in faded green silk. It began, 'He who has everything, sometimes has nothing.'

The Meatball's Fate

ONCE UPON A TIME there was a large tray of meatballs sizzling away in the oven. As the heat grew worse and worse and the oven got hotter and hotter, they cried out to their leader, the biggest meatball of them all, 'O great Meatball Leader, we will do anything you say and give you all our allegiance for the rest of our lives, if only you will save us and get us out of this oven.'

'Very well,' said the largest meatball. 'I will bring all of my mind to bear on the subject and I will get you out of the oven.'

'Oh! oh! oh!' cried the meatballs, 'our bodies are burning.'

'Have no fear,' said the chief meatball. 'I will see to it that you will have cooling medicine for your burns and beds of soft sweet-smelling rice upon which to lie.'

No sooner had he said this than the door of the oven opened; the meatballs were laid on a very large dish of flavoured rice and a red tomato sauce was poured all over them.

'Great and wonderful Meatball Leader,' cried the meatballs in unison, 'you have saved us, just as you said you would. Oh how delightful to us is this cooling red liquid and how remarkably soft is this white substance upon which we are now lying.'

'Of course,' responded the leader of the meatballs. 'Did I not promise? And what I promise, you can always be sure will happen in the fullness of time.'

Suddenly the meatballs began to feel terribly frightened again, and they looked around to see that many of their number were being spooned onto plates; even as they watched, meatballs were being forked up, covered in tomato sauce and eaten!

'Evil and perfidious Meatball Leader,' shouted the remaining meatballs. 'How could we ever have trusted you? What is happening to us? Why are our numbers being so horribly reduced? Explain, before we all die in this abominable way.'

'My friends,' said the leader of the meatballs calmly, even as rice was being piled onto him so that he could hardly be heard. 'I got you out of the oven as you desired. I arranged that soothing liquids be poured upon your burns. Were there not vast quantities of rice upon which you could lie?'

'Yes, yes,' squeaked the last meatball, 'but why, why this terrible end?'

'Well,' said the giant meatball as the rice covered him from view, 'is it not the fate, the kismet, of all meatballs to be, in fact, actually eaten?'

There came no answer for surely, as you will understand, there never could be one in those circumstances.

The Emerald Scorpion

ONCE UPON A TIME in the land of Hindustan there lived a powerful Raja. He had many valuable ropes of pearls to wear around his neck on great occasions, fabulous fitted coats of embroidered gold brocade, and a hundred turbans of finest silk, each more beautiful and colourful than the feathers of the sacred peacock which the Raja believed was inhabited by the soul of his grandfather. He had several wives in his long life, each from a different part of India, and courtiers who told him exactly what he wanted to hear — that he was excessively handsome, tremendously wealthy and fantastically clever. He threw coins to the poor every morning from his balcony, accepted presents from the rich on the occasion of his birthday and any other occasion which the donors could think of, and generally enjoyed himself from morning to night.

But there was one snag: he had no son. His various wives had produced nothing but daughters so, now that his daughters were of marriageable age, it took him much time each month to send several of them away to be married. He had himself married at the most propitious time of year, and in each case they had been exquisite ladies, doe-eyed, wide-hipped, and of the highest degree. Once he had even married a beautiful milkmaid, so beloved of the Lord Krishna, but the issue was a daughter just the same.

But a man must have a son to see that he is dispatched in the right way after death, one who would attend to all the rites with true devotion; and how was the line to be carried on without a son? He did not know just how many small female creatures there were in that rambling palace, with jewels in their ears and in their noses, who called him father. Even leaving aside the daughters he had married off, he could still count quite a number of girls produced by his Ranis, each of whom, he had to admit, had tried her very best.

He called his advisor, Nandi, to him one morning as he was choosing which necklace to wear just after the disbursal to the poor.

'Tell me, Nandi,' he asked the slightly nervous retainer, who never knew what the Raja was going to ask next. 'Tell me, is there any specially wise man whom you know of, who might come here and tell me why I have not got a son? It is getting a bit late, you know, for this morning I very distinctly saw a white hair — my very first white hair — in my beard.'

'Your Highness,' said Nandi, 'I venture to suggest the advice of a certain wise sadhu being sought, a most holy man who can sometimes be prevailed upon to travel from his cave and to speak the truth to potentates without even charging a fee. For he has the gift of prophesy and wants to help people who have trouble in this life, be they high-born or low-born.'

The Raja adjusted his jewels and put his turban at an angle.

'What is his name? Get him at once and I will reward him generously,' he said.

The advisor told him, 'His name is Pal, Your Highness, and he will be here in three days' time if I send a messenger for him today. He will tell you why you have no son and if it is possible for Your Highness to have one.'

'Go! Saddle the fastest horse in the stables! Send the messenger quickly!' cried the Raja in great excitement, and Nandi hurried away.

For three days and nights the Raja anxiously awaited the

arrival of the holy man, and during that time he scarcely ate or slept. When finally he dozed off for a few minutes in the heat of noon on the third day, it was only to be awoken by the ever-nervous Nandi.

'Your Highness, Your Highness, please forgive me. I am so sorry to have to awake you but the holy sadhu, Pal, has come. He is sitting in the courtyard below — now that the place has been purified with incense sticks by the senior Rani. You did say that I was to wake you as soon as he came.'

'Oh, excellent!' said the Raja. 'Get me my turban with the diamond and ruby pin and I will go down to him at once.'

In less time than it takes to tell, the Raja was seated on the throne with his eyes fixed on the sadhu, who was squatting on a saffron cloth, eyes shut, a curious mark on his unlined brow, his palms upturned on his knees. He seemed to be asleep, but as the Raja cleared his throat gently to indicate his presence, the old holy man opened his eyes. They were of a most remarkable brilliance, like brown agate, and they held the Raja's for a long moment in an unwavering, unblinking stare. The Raja sat nervously twiddling his jewels.

'Speak, O Raja, ask your question. I am prepared to answer,' intoned the sadhu.

'Why have I fathered only daughters? Is there a woman alive who can be the mother of my son?' asked the Raja with deep feeling.

The old man sighed, expelling a great breath from his lungs. When he had inhaled slowly, he said, 'Raja, you are under a spell. Until that spell is lifted you will have only daughters. It is none of your doing, but the action of those who came before you. Thus is the wheel of Karma set in motion and has its effect upon the lives of all those who come after.'

'A spell? What sort of a spell?' cried the Raja. 'How can I get free of this terrible thing and beget a son who can see me to the funeral pyre and beyond to a new life?'

'You will have a son when that harmful object which you have in your treasury now is returned to its rightful owner,' said the sadhu.

'What is this accursed thing of which you speak?' cried the Raja. 'Tell me and I will take it back myself, even if the journey be beyond the very furthest borders of India.'

Once more the old man took some moments to answer and then he said, 'It is a scorpion, an emerald scorpion which brings you bad luck. Your grandfather acquired the jewel in some devious arrangement, about a hundred years ago. It was the luck of a certain family, a family whose name was as great as your own. Without it, their fortunes have failed. Return it to them. Marry the daughter of the house and I tell you with the power invested in me that, within a year, you will be the proud father of a son.'

The sadhu closed his eyes and the Raja saw that the message was at an end.

'Oh happy day! Oh most auspicious bearer of life-giving news!' shouted the Raja. 'I will cause your august mouth to be filled with jewels You shall never want to the end of your days. I will build you a palace…'

Then he stopped as he saw that what he was saying was making the old man quite angry.

'Oh, please forgive me, pious father,' he said. 'I realise I am offering you things which, to you, are a mortification. What can I do to repay you? Only do us the great honour of eating something here.'

The old man rose from the ground and wrapped himself in his saffron cloth. 'I have everything I need,' he said. 'It is you who want. Take the emerald scorpion back to the Maharaja who lives in the wooden palace near the Crocodile River. Marry his daughter and you will get your wish.'

And with a pleasant smile, the ancient wise man made to walk away, his feet scarcely seeming to touch the earth.

The Raja in his rich attire himself took the sadhu to the royal kitchens. Thanking him most profusely he, with his own hands, put upon a wooden platter some simple fare which was all the holy man would allow him to give in return for the strange message.

Then the Raja sped as fast as was possible for one in his elevated position, to the vast treasury beneath the palace. With his trusted treasurer, Randas, he searched the caskets in the vaults until he himself discovered the emerald scorpion carved out of one flawless brilliant green stone.

'Let us ride to the wooden palace,' cried the Raja in glee. Riding his favourite steed, with his mounted bodyguard surrounding him, the Raja set off to see the Maharaja who lived in the old wooden palace near the Crocodile River.

When he got there, the Raja thought he had come to a ruin, but at last he was admitted into the presence of the impoverished Maharaja, Ram Singh. His only daughter, a pretty, plump young thing, was sitting in the window stringing beads.

'I have something of great importance to give you, O Maharaja,' said the visitor when both were sitting side by side on a carved sandalwood seat. He placed the emerald scorpion in the other's hand, saying, 'Let the luck of your family be returned to you. I have been told by a holy man that one of my ancestors deprived your family of this, and I am now returning it. May the gods give us all blessings because of this act.'

No sooner did the Maharaja take the jewel into his own hand than the derelict palace became as new once more, covered with gold leaf as it had been a hundred years before, and with a thousand lamps shining in every niche. Flower garlands miraculously appeared on the necks of the Raja and the Maharaja and singing birds in golden cages hung at every window. Beautiful maids brought them the finest of foods and precious scents wafted down from the balcony where the Ranis sat. The sound of music came from the courtyard and peacocks strutted through the rooms of the palace, rivalling the gorgeous silks of the ladies. The Maharaja's daughter was dressed in bridal attire and led to where the Raja was sitting.

'Take my daughter as your wife, my dear friend,' cried the Maharaja.

And the wedding was celebrated without delay.

In a year's time, the Raja became the very proud father of a son, one of three he was to have from his lovely young wife.

And that is the end of the tale of the emerald scorpion.

❧ROMANY TALES❧

The Story of Carrot Top

ONCE UPON A TIME in a Romany encampment, there lived a boy with bright red hair. He had three brothers and two sisters, and all were possessed of hair as dark as a raven's wing, so he was known as Carrot Top. Nobody ever called him Joe, which was his real name, but he did not mind. It was fun being different. He always thought that the children from the other Romany families must be right when they said that his mother had found him when she was blackberrying in the woods twelve years before. But whether he was a foundling or not didn't make any difference to the affection his family had for him.

His greatest pleasure was in carving little animals out of wood and whenever he was able to go away by himself, he would look for dry roots or pieces of wood, which he would immediately know were right for one of his carvings. His mother and sisters made pegs to sell in the nearby town, and his father had been dead long since. All the children, even the youngest who was six years old, helped to sort out rags to sell to a man who came in his cart once a month from the town.

Life was fun for Carrot Top. There was never time to be bored for he was always doing something interesting. The woods by his family's caravan were full of tall pine trees, spruces, hazel and fir, and at each season of the year, there was always some fun for the children. It never seemed like work to collect fat, shiny black-berries, eating one or two as their quick, suntanned hands darted in and out of the leaves.

One day, when they were all in the town, there came a tall,

beautifully dressed lady in a carriage drawn by two fine horses. She looked at the small, tattered mob of children hopping and skipping beside the marble drinking fountain.

'Stop the carriage, George,' she said, stepping down. 'Come here, you little red-haired gypsy,' she called in a sweet voice and crooked her finger at Carrot Top. The other children stopped playing and crowded around the lady; jewels glittered in her small, shell-like ears and the red ruby on her finger glistened like a blood-red star.

'Come here. Tell me your name,' she said.

Carrot Top looked at her, and for a moment it seemed as if she were the sort of fairy queen that he had only imagined in his dreams, for he had never seen such a fine lady before in his life. He could scarcely speak, but the other children pushed him forward and he found himself looking into her eyes, which were as green as the leaves in spring. Her hair, bound in a silver net, was reddish-gold, like the tiger lilies which grew in his own secret clearing in the depths of the woods.

'My name's Little Joe,' he said. But the other children went into peals of laughter and shouted out, 'No, no, he's only Carrot Top.'

He felt himself blushing red as fire when they said that. This was the very first time that he had ever been ashamed of his nickname. The tall, beautiful, golden-haired lady laughed and put her hand, with its great red jewel, on his shoulder.

'Don't mind them,' she said. 'That's what my brothers always used to call me and I know how you feel, but you know, we carrot tops are something different, so be proud of that.' Little Joe felt better when he heard this and his heart swelled with pleasure.

'I can sell twice as many nuts and berries and mushrooms as

the others,' he said. 'My hair doesn't seem to make any difference there.' And his eyes shone with pride.

At that moment his mother returned with his older sister, and he could see that they had sold all their pegs. Their big baskets were full of groceries. It was time to go, so, rather unwillingly, he turned away from the lady and made his way towards them. The lady called, 'Little Joe, don't go. I want to ask you something. Would you like to come and work for me in my house in the town? Come — let me talk to your mother about it.'

Carrot Top's mother stopped and stood in front of the lady, her black hair pinned up at the back with gleaming silver combs. She was wearing her red blouse and a velvet skirt, all sewn with different coloured squares, her boots black and patched and wrinkled like prunes.

'Lady, how could you teach our Joey to live in a house, bless you, your ladyship? He's never slept between sheets or under a heavy old roof of tiles,' she laughed, showing all her gold-filled teeth in a most bewitching smile. Her hoop earring looked like a new moon. She had lost the other one long ago and never managed to replace it. She had been given the earrings as a wedding present the night she lit the wedding fire with big Joe. That night she had felt as proud as a queen because she had always wanted to live in her own caravan, away from her large family of brothers and sisters, and to have her own family.

So they stood there, the tall slim lady in her fine clothes and elegant boots, her skin as white as milk and as pink as strawberries, and the sun-tanned Romany with the wisdom of India in her dark eyes. Between them stood Carrot Top, looking from one to the other with his mind in a whirl. But these two women were sisters under their skin, and the lady soon convinced the Romany that it would be greatly to Carrot Top's advantage to go with her. She promised that any time his mother wanted to see him she could come to the great house. Also, that any time he wanted to return to the woods he could do so with her blessing. The long and the short of it was that when the carriage turned about and drove off with its spanking horses, Little Joe was inside waving to his mother and the rest of the children, with his heart beating wildly.

The lady sat opposite him in the carriage, smiling at him gently, and Carrot Top sat with his arms tightly folded across his chest as if it was the only way to keep himself and his new-found good luck together.

Soon they arrived in the driveway of a great house with tall chimneys, and there were servants opening and closing doors and large dogs wagging their tails in welcome at the lady's return. Maids dressed in white aprons and lace caps were curtseying all over the place. The dogs sniffed at him and seemed unsure whether he was one of them or something they had never seen before. Carrot Top felt that no-one quite understood who he was or what he was doing there. The maids all giggled when the mistress told them to take Little Joe away and show him where he was to sleep — it was a nice, small room looking onto a large garden with plants in huge white marble urns, peacocks strolling along green lawns, and strange-looking ducks floating on an elegant lake.

In less time than it takes to tell, Joe was washed from top to toe in a huge tin bath, given some clothes which just about fitted him and taken to the servants' dining room to eat with the staff. He felt small and rather strange as he ate his first meal. Now, Joe, as you know, had never lived in a house, so he felt very odd that night when he was taken to his small, dark bedroom with a candle in a pewter candlestick in his hand, and the door was closed behind him.

He felt trapped and he wanted to cry, 'Let me go, let me out into the garden!' But he dared not make an uproar in the lady's house, so he waited until everyone had gone to their own beds. Then he took the rough, grey blanket which was on top of the small wooden bed and silently he crept out into the garden. There he wrapped himself in the blanket, lay looking at the stars and finally fell asleep under a bush. In the morning he was up very early, washed his face and hands in the pond, and stared at the big house from the foot of the white alabaster steps, which shone like the sugar loaves he had seen in the grocer's shop, and started to climb them. He reached the balcony and peered into the house from outside. As his eyes got used to the gloom inside, he began to make out shapes which looked huge to him.

There were large silver candlesticks with gigantic wax candles looking like those on the church altar. There were bright china vases as tall as himself with peculiar dragons and flying things on them. There were curtains sewn with golden flowers more strange than any he had ever seen growing in the depths of the woods.

As he was walking back to the room where he had been supposed to sleep, the head servant pounced on him and asked sternly, 'Where have you been? What were you doing? You must behave properly and not like a stupid gypsy.'

Carrot Top could not do anything but stand there rooted to the spot, clutching his grey blanket.

'Well, shoot off now. Get yourself washed and dressed, neat and tidy. You must start working in earnest now, as we all do.'

That first day at work in the kitchens of the big house was very difficult for Carrot Top. He never knew what it was they were asking him to find and bring to them. Curious objects hung on hooks around the walls, unlike anything he had ever seen before, and his eyes grew larger and larger as he stared around. His mind was in a whirl. By the time he was through all his duties he was so tired that he fell asleep on the floor of his small room, while waiting for the others to retire so that he could go and sleep out of doors.

Gradually, he became trained to do what was expected of him, though not tamed in the way the servants required him to be. They looked down their noses most of the time and did not even appear to be at ease with each other, though of course, every time that they went upstairs to wait on the lady of the house, they put on what Carrot Top called their false faces.

He was always hoping that one day his mother would come and visit him and that he could give her the money which the grand butler gave him every week. He put it all in a wash-leather bag which he kept under the wooden bed in his room. He was hoping that he would soon have enough to buy another golden earring for his mother, so that she could be like all the other Romanies and swing a bright moon of gold from both ears.

The days and the weeks went by and his mother did not come. He knew from that first journey in the horse carriage on the day he had arrived, that it would be miles and miles through strange country for him to return to his own woods. The caravan where his mother and family lived was far, far away, so he waited for his mother to come to him.

The seasons were changing fast. Carrot Top knew that the end of the year was coming — yet still he didn't feel that he would ever fit into that peculiar household. Often there were days when he felt like running away, but he didn't know where to go. Then he remembered that the lady had said that he could go back to his mother's woods any time he liked; but he could never summon up enough courage to ask.

One day, Carrot Top suddenly felt that he wanted to see his mother and brothers and sisters more than anything else in the world. He made up his mind to run away that very night when everyone was fast asleep. Wherever it was that his mother and the Romany caravan were located, he felt sure that he would find them. He put the wash-leather bag around his neck, his whittling knife in his belt and went into the garden. He made his way to the great gates and peered upwards, looking to see how he could get over. Just as he was deciding where to begin, there was a hoarse shout from the gatekeeper, who waved him away.

'I know you rascally gypsy boys. Get out of there! What are you doing prowling around at this time of night?'

Carrot Top faded into the shadows. There was now no chance of getting over the gate unseen, so he began to work his way around, along the inside of the garden wall. Just as he had found a place where he might get a grip on the rough stone, he heard growling and saw two very large hounds coming towards him. Their great gleaming eyes were getting nearer and nearer and the rumbling from their throats grew louder and louder.

Walking backwards very carefully, Carrot Top found he was at the bottom of a vast and ancient tree, with branches sweeping the ground. He managed to get onto one of the branches by swinging himself into the air like a monkey, just like he used to do in his own woods. He climbed to a higher branch and then to another until he was well out of the way of the hounds, though he could see their sharp white teeth gleaming in the darkness below and hear their terrifying growls. Carrot Top settled down to wait until the dogs lost interest in him and went away. Eventually, he must have dozed off, his back against the comforting trunk of the tree, his legs braced firmly and his hands grasping the bough in front of him.

Suddenly he awoke. It was quite dark and very cold. Grey clouds had obscured the face of the moon. Carrot Top yawned and looked around him. There was no sign of the dogs. All was silent in the garden. Wondering what to do, Carrot Top flexed his muscles, trying to stretch one leg and then the other. He felt that something really exciting was about to happen — and it did.

His ears caught a familiar sound which gradually grew louder, a sound he knew so well — the clip clop of the hooves of his mother's caravan. From where he sat in the huge tree, Carrot Top could see the roof of the house in which he had been such an unhappy inmate for the past few months, with the frost lying thick upon it. Shivering in his thin clothes, he began to move down a branch of the tree which overhung the road, hand over hand, foot by foot, till he was perched right over the road. He saw the brightly painted wagon coming, the pinto horse with its distinctive markings showing up on the frosty road, its hooves ringing on the iron-hard ground.

Nearer and nearer it came, and Carrot Top could see his mother seated on the steps of the wagon with the reins in her hands. He tried to call out, but his voice did not come — he made no sound. Perhaps that was just as well for, had he done so, there might have been someone to hear and try to drag him back from his hiding place. As he hung over the road he saw the wagon stop beneath him. He swung his legs down and felt his feet touch the roof; he dropped down, swayed and then righted himself.

'Welcome home Joe, my son,' said his mother's voice. And he

climbed in at the window of the caravan.

He saw his brothers and sisters lying tucked up, fast sleep, so he climbed over them until he reached the space beside his mother, who clicked her tongue to the horse to make it start off again. The moon shone on its harness and the silver ornaments hanging from the bridle. His mother turned her dark Indian eyes to his, and her one golden earring swung in the lobe of her left ear, which was turned towards him.

Carrot Top pressed the wash-leather bag which contained his earnings into his mother's hand.

'What's this for, my dear?' she asked.

'For you to buy yourself another earring,' he said proudly, taking the reins from her. 'I'm back now, Mother. Go inside the wagon and lie down. Which way are we going?'

'South,' said his mother. 'Always south at this time of year. You know how cold the woods get when the snows come. We're going to Spain.'

His mother got down, climbed inside the wagon and lay down to sleep.

Inside the great house a little way back up the road, the beautiful lady turned over in her linen sheets while the servants below stairs snored or tossed and turned, each according to their condition. The huge white moon shone down on them and she shone on Carrot Top, happiest of Romanies — the Romany with red hair who would never, never in all his long life have to sleep under a roof again.

The Silver Ring of Black Lopez

ONCE UPON A TIME, long ago, when the black virgin of Barcelona had just been set in the cathedral, there lived a Spanish Romany called Pedro. He was one of the best harness-makers in the whole of Spain, and everyone would come to him for bridles, halters, reins and every type of harness for horses. But he had the worst memory in all the world, and every year he forgot his wife, Maria Teresa's, birthday which annoyed her intensely. When he did remember to give her a present it was usually too late, and she got very angry. So, one year, he decided to tie a knot in his red spotted handkerchief a few days in advance, so that when he looked at the knot he would know that on the night of the full moon, it was his wife's right to expect a present from him.

Well, on this evening of which we speak, some Romany friends had asked him to play cards. The game grew fast and furious, and then they played another and then another, until suddenly it was time for Pedro to go home. And, of course, he had forgotten all about buying a present for his wife's birthday once more, in spite of the knot that he had tied in the red spotted handkerchief.

'Maria Teresa will black my eyes for sure this time,' he thought, as he wandered somewhat unsteadily towards his caravan, parked for the time being on the outskirts of the town, till the Romanies should get the urge to go on elsewhere. Suddenly, the unhappy Pedro stumbled on something which lay across his path, a something which caught the moonlight and which after a few moments' scrutiny he recognised as the sleeping figure of Black Lopez, the Romany peddler. He seemed to be sleeping very deeply. But when Pedro knelt on the ground beside him and felt his pulse it was obvious that he was dead — there was no flicker of life left in his thin wrist.

'Oh, poor fellow,' murmured Pedro. 'But it's time he was gone for he must have been very old. I've seen him selling his wares up and down the country ever since I was a boy.'

Then his eye was caught by a bright silver ring on the little finger of old Lopez's right hand. The moonlight caught it and it shone brighter than any ring Pedro had ever seen. He quickly looked around to see if there was anyone looking and then he pulled the ring off the old, withered finger.

'I'll give this to Maria Teresa for her birthday present,' he told himself gleefully. 'Black Lopez will never need it again, I'll be bound. He can't wear it where he's gone.' And he slipped the ring into his pocket.

When he saw three Romany men approaching, he called to them: 'Hey, brothers, look. I've just found old Black Lopez dead. Let's take him to the priest so that he can say a few words over him. He's got no kith or kin so we'll bury him and burn his caravan tomorrow and his goods will go with him to the next world.' The four men carried Black Lopez to the priest to arrange the burial, and afterwards Pedro returned to home to tell his wife all about it.

Then he presented her with the silver ring, not telling her, however, where he had got it. Maria Teresa was delighted with the present, and gave him a kiss on both cheeks instead of the two black eyes he had anticipated before he acquired the ring. They went to bed as happy as the wind and the stars. But in the middle of the night, as the owls hooted and grey, restless clouds flew across the face of the moon, Pedro woke and sat bolt upright in his caravan. He had heard a noise at the door; now he heard someone moaning in a low voice:

'Give me back my ring, Pedro. Give me back my ring or I can never rest and I will haunt you all your life long.'

'Who… who… who… who is it?' cried Pedro fearfully.

The answer came back, 'Black Lopez, Black Lopez, the peddler whom you robbed tonight.'

Pedro looked around fearfully to see if his wife had heard, but she was still sleeping and he cried, 'Go away. You don't need any silver ring where you are, Black Lopez. Tomorrow your caravan and all its contents are to be burned so that you will have everything with you. Can you not forget about one little silver ring?'

'No, no, no,' moaned the ghost. 'And I will haunt you till your last day if you do not give it back.'

'Nonsense,' said Pedro as bravely as he could, but his lips were dry and his eyes were starting out of his head. 'I gave your ring to my wife as a birthday present, as I knew you had no further use for it.'

Suddenly the top half of the caravan door flew open, and though Pedro could see nothing he heard the sound of bones rattling across the floor. The skeletal hand of Black Lopez knocked on the floorboards and the ghostly voice said, 'Give me back my ring, Pedro, or I shall have to come and pull it off your wife's finger myself.'

'No, no, no. Don't do that! She'll never forgive me. And stop all that groaning and moaning and knocking,' pleaded Pedro, 'or you will wake her and I shall never hear the end of it.'

Rattle, rattle, rattle went the bones of Black Lopez as his

white skeleton danced before Pedro's eyes. 'Only you can see me, Pedro,' said the chattering teeth of Black Lopez. 'Give me back my silver ring and I will go and leave you in peace. Your wife will never know that I have been, for I have the magical power to make her forget that you ever gave her the ring,' said the ghost of the old peddler.

'All right, then,' said Pedro, and he pulled the ring off his wife's finger as her hand lay on the coverlet. 'Take your silver ring, Black Lopez, and please forgive me. I hope that you will rest in Heaven and never trouble me again. I beg your forgiveness. I know I should never, never have taken your ring.'

'Very well, I will forgive you,' said the low, moaning voice; and for a few seconds the ring shone on the little finger of Black Lopez's right hand. The teeth of the skeleton seemed to smile and then, with a rattle of bones, the ghost disappeared altogether.

'Merciful Heavens,' cried the Romany. 'I hope he keeps his word. I couldn't stand another fright like that again.'

Just then Pedro's wife woke and, as the ghost had eradicated the memory of the ring from her mind, she raised herself up on one elbow and screamed at her husband, 'So, you've come back home at last have you — and forgotten to bring me a present again, have you? Well, take that, and take that!' And she swiftly blacked both of poor Pedro's eyes.

But Pedro was so glad to have got rid of the ghost and so pleased that Maria Teresa would never know about the silver ring, that there was a smile on his bruised face as he lay back on his pillow. As for the ghost of Lopez, he was as good as his word, for Pedro never saw or heard the rattle of his skeleton again.

The Mayfly

ONCE UPON A TIME there was a mayfly — one of those little flies which only lives one day. Its whole life consisted of being born when the sun shone on its egg and playing about in the warmth and the shadows, skimming the surface of the water of its own home pond. But, on this particular day, it fell into a milk pan.

Now this mayfly, as soon as it felt that it was out of its depth in that thick, creamy milk, called out in a very thin and squeaky voice, 'Oh hear me, great Lord of the World. Get me out of this milkpan for else I shall surely die and never enjoy anything of the fine life before me.' And it sent a prayer with all the power of its being into the void.

At that moment the cook saw that there was a tiny black speck in the milkpan and flicked it out onto the table with a spoon, saying in a loud, gruff voice, 'Out of that milk, you beastly little fly. You have nearly ruined my beautiful sauce.' Then he poured some of the milk into the concoction he was preparing for his mistress's meal.

The mayfly, finding itself on dry land, raised up its tiny little voice and cried, 'Thank you! Thank you for saving me in the very nick of time, great Lord of the World. I heard your earth-shattering voice as you saved me, though of course I could never understand the language of one so great as you.'

It began to dry its tiny wings in the sun and rubbed the milk off its legs, doing a crazy dance in the sunshine — then it launched itself off the table and into the air.

'I shall of course devote myself to the saving of humanity and doing good for the rest of my days,' the mayfly continued. 'But today, I am a little exhausted by my great experience so I will start my tremendous task tomorrow.'

Which of course was a completely useless remark for, as we all know, a mayfly lives for only one day.

The Magic Peg Basket

ONCE UPON A TIME, there was born the prettiest girl that you could ever set eyes upon, into the family of a handsome Romany travelling man. Her big, brown eyes had long lashes that you could catch tiddlers with, and all the Romany mothers wanted her for their sons. Her name was Rosie Lee and you couldn't have finer luck in this life than to be a Lee, for the gift of the second sight is given to them and many more things besides. Many Lees live to be a hundred years old, have seven sons, and tell the fortunes of all the kings and queens that are now left in the world.

One day, when she was about sixteen or seventeen years old, as slim as a hazel twig and as light on her feet as a grasshopper, she took her grandmother's old peg basket full of her best pegs to sell in the town. It was spring, and all the houses were shining in the bright sunlight. She knocked on the door of a very fine house right in the middle of the grandest street in town. It had a huge brass lion's head for a door-knocker, and no sooner had she just tapped it, than the window above flew open and a fat-faced dame in a bright yellow wig thrust her head out and asked, 'What would you be selling, my dear?'

Rosie Lee answered with a smile, 'Pegs, lady, and a little bit of white heather to bring you luck for the rest of the week.'

'Oh, I must have some pegs and a bit of the good luck,' said the fat-faced lady. And down she came and opened the door.

Well, once the door was opened, Rosie saw that inside was just like a palace, for though, to be sure, she had never seen a palace in all her life, she knew that this was what a palace should be like, with the great brass candle-sticks on the polished table in the hall and carpets that must have cost a king's ransom under her boots on the floor.

'Come in, come in, child,' said the dame, who was the house-keeper there. She took Rosie further down the hall and unlike most of the women in the town, she never said, 'To the back door and mind the mud off your boots. Don't get it on to my clean floor!'

With her grandmother's peg basket on her arm, Rosie found herself turning around and around, like a teetotum, wanting to see all those great treasures — vases as high as herself made of Chinese porcelain, paintings of fine ladies and gentlemen in beautiful clothes, rich curtains tied back from the windows with silk embroidered bands.

The housekeeper chose twenty of Rosie's best handmade pegs and then a sprig of the lucky white heather. She was just paying for them with money from the purse hanging at her waist, when Rosie heard a cough and saw a tall, dark, thin gentleman descending the stairs. He was dressed very plainly and wore a long black cloak, which seemed to be lined with red silk. The housekeeper got all flustered and dropped the gentleman a curtsey. Rosie bobbed up and down too, and as she looked at him with her big brown eyes, the tall gentleman twirled his long black moustache and said, 'Ah ha, Mrs. Anthropos, and what have we here?'

'Tis a Romany child, Your Honour,' said the housekeeper, 'and I do apologize for bringing her into the hall, for I truly thought that Your Honour was out of the house long ago.'

The gentleman smiled. Rosie thought that she had never seen such bright white teeth or such strange brilliant eyes. He bent to look at her as he reached the foot of the stairs.

'Not at all bad, Mrs. Anthropos,' he said with a charming smile. 'I'm delighted that you show so much humanity as to bring in this delightful creature. Be so good as to bring two cups of chocolate to my study. I would like to have a talk with her there.'

Hypnotised by his eyes, Rosie Lee followed him into a room to the right of the stairs, and sat on the chair indicated by her host while Mrs. Anthropos hurried away to do her master's bidding.

'I have just a few minutes to make your acquaintance,' said the tall, dark gentleman, walking lightly to the big armchair beside the fireplace. As he threw back his long cape lined with red silk, Rosie's grip on her peg basket tightened with fear as she saw that he was possessed of a pair of cloven hoofs instead of feet.

'Yes, my dear,' smiled the Devil as he crossed one knee over the other, 'most people call me Satan, or Old Nick, and many other rather uncomplimentary names, but that doesn't mean that I cannot be quite interesting to know, does it?'

'Do you… do you live here all by yourself, sir?' asked Rosie as politely as she could, wondering whatever had made her come into this room and why she was sitting so calmly talking to Satan as if she had known him all her life!

'Yes, I do live here by myself at the moment, and it is getting a bit lonely, but I have a lot of business to attend to in the town, especially at night. I am always glad to get to bed while I am on one of these trips to earth,' said the Devil quite serenely, as if he were an ordinary businessman.

Mrs. Anthropos now appeared with chocolate in two beautiful china cups which she placed on the table and then, discreetly, she vanished. The chocolate was perfectly delicious and the cups were soon empty. The tall, dark man looked at his gold pocket watch:

'Oh, it's later than I thought,' he said. 'Please forgive me. I must be off. Mrs. Anthropos will see you out and if you are ever this way again, please do drop in.'

Before Rosie could blink he was gone, disappearing into thin air, and there was a distinct smell of sulphur in the room.

Mrs. Anthropos came in then and showed Rosie out of the house. Rosie went on her way, selling pegs at some houses and white heather at others, just as if it were an ordinary day.

That night when she got back to the caravan, Rosie told her mother the story from beginning to end, and Mrs. Lee looked rather distressed.

'Oh dear me, Rosie,' she said. 'It sounds to me as if he's taken a bit of a fancy to you and that's not a healthy thing, not a healthy thing at all.'

'Why, Mother, do you think I shall ever see him again? I won't go near that house, I promise you that,' said she, 'and I wouldn't mind not going out on the street selling until he's forgotten all about me.'

'It's not as easy as all that, love,' said Mrs. Lee. 'Satan's bound to know where you are, and if he wants to find you, he will. Now let me remember. Get me your grandmother's peg basket. It's got a bit of magic in it, I recall.'

Rosie fetched the peg basket and her mother emptied out all the remaining pegs. 'If his Satanic Majesty should pay you a visit,' said she, 'hold this over his head. Say "Boobajoobs" very quickly and he'll be turned into something as small as your thumb. Then call me!'

That very night, when the campfire had died back and the bats were dashing around the roof of the ruined house just outside the town where the Romanies had their camp, the tall, dark Devil appeared on the steps of the caravan where Rosie slept with her smaller brothers and sisters. He knocked three times on the door.

Rosie was ready for him. She opened the door and smilingly wished him good evening. Then, holding the magic peg basket over his head, she cried out, 'Boobajoobs!' as quickly as she could.

'I've come to ask you to be my wife, Rosie,' the Devil was just beginning to say, but he had shrunk to the size of your thumb by the time he had finished and, when Rosie's mother came in answer to her call, he was stamping about on the ground under the caravan, squeaking with rage.

'Turn me back to my normal size at once,' shrieked the Devil, 'you abominable Romany witch! I might have known better than to meddle with any of you.'

'If you will promise never to come near my daughter again or try to tempt her in any way for the rest of her life,' said Mrs. Lee, looking down as though from a great height onto the tiny Devil at her feet, 'I'll let you go back to your own size, but you'll have to swear the oath in Romany and if you break it you will never be any bigger than a pin head until Judgment Day.'

She held the magic peg basket over his head and, spluttering with annoyance, the Devil agreed. She knelt down on the ground and murmured the words of the Romany oath into his ear. The Devil repeated the oath and his promise and within a very few minutes he had shot up to his own size again. This time there was a very strong smell of sulphur in the air when he disappeared.

Mrs. Lee clapped her hands and touched all the charms hanging around her neck one by one, saying magic words under her breath. 'Now you're safe, Rosie my girl,' she said. 'But I think you had better marry your cousin, Rubin Lee, as soon as we can arrange it, for the Devil is not to be trusted where there are young unmarried maids about.'

Rosie smiled, for she had always thought of Rubin as her husband ever since she was a small girl — she looked forward to marrying him. Still grinning to herself, she picked up the magic peg basket and took it into the caravan with her. As she did so she thought: 'That cup of chocolate was the sweetest thing I have ever tasted in all my life and likely to be the sweetest thing I ever shall taste.' And do you know, I think she was right.

The Romany who Married
a Bird Woman

OW ONCE THERE WAS A ROMANY who fell in love with a bird, and I will tell you all about it. This Romany was an Irish one, and a finer looking fellow you could never wish to see in the whole of the Emerald Isle. He was six foot and a bit tall, with thick black hair and a pair of bold, black eyes. He had a fine painted wagon with a fat old horse to take him around, and her name was Nora.

'Come along Nora, my dear,' said he one day as she was ambling along the road beside the biggest stretch of water that he had ever seen in his life. 'Let's get to that spot under the trees and I'll be letting you out of the shafts for a good meal of fine, green grass and it won't be long before my sausages will be jumping about in the pan, I can tell you that.'

So while Nora was cropping the grass and a fire of twigs was heating the frying pan, this Romany fellow, whose name was Mike, looked out across the great lake and thought it was a really beautiful sight. He had travelled up and down the fair face of Ireland all his life since he had inherited this grand, green wagon from his uncle Romany Dan. He was contented and happy with his lot, for he never wanted for anything while his good dog Jess could bring him a fat rabbit for the pot whenever he felt like it — and he carried on the family tradition of shoeing horses, and doctoring them too, when he had to.

Mike was looking out over the lake and contemplating his

meal when a great flock of white geese landed on its beautiful, calm waters. As the light caught the birds, they looked like so many lovely women, all taking a dip at the same time.

As he looked harder, he almost dropped the pan in surprise, but just managed to hold on to it — remembering that if he dropped his meal, old Jess would eat it as quick as look at him. So, pan in hand, he walked towards the lake. For there, bathing with their heads just above water, their arms waving in the air, doing their hair and such, were about fifty or sixty beautiful young girls. They didn't seem to notice him at all, perhaps because they didn't think there would be anyone else but themselves around. He could hear their cries of joy and happy shrieking as they threw water over themselves and over each other.

He watched for about fifteen minutes and then they all seemed to leap out of the water together as they flew off into the sky.

'By all that is holy,' gasped Mike, flinging himself down and eating his meal, throwing two of the sausages to the dog who gulped them down. 'Now if I hadn't seen them with me own eyes and in bright daylight, I would never have believed this if I had been told it by anyone at all.'

He stayed there by the lake that night and mended a harness or two in the morning, looking over the beautiful water and admiring the view; but the geese did not return that day. However, on the following day, just as he was harnessing Nora, he heard the rush of wings in the sky above. Looking up, he saw the flock of gleaming white geese descending to the surface of the lake. So he hid behind a tree and watched. Yes, there they were, all turning into young women again before his very eyes, and soon their happy laughter came to him, carried on the breeze from the lake.

One girl was lovelier than all the rest — a beautiful, pale-skinned creature with a long white neck and an oval face, crowned with tendrils of wet, black hair. He watched as she came out of the water and preened herself, arching her neck. Then, giving a musical laugh, she changed into a feathered bird and flew away with the others all following her.

'Oh, what a delicate lady! What a princess, what a queen! If only I too could be a goose and fly away with them,' Mike thought.

He could not leave that place until he had seen her again, he told himself. So he waited one more day.

The birds arrived at the same time as before, had their swim and preened themselves, but this time Mike rushed down to the shore of the lake. Catching the lovely goose maiden by the arm, he blurted out, 'Oh, dearest princess, do not fly away again. I want you to stay and be with me here. I have never in all my life seen anyone as beautiful as you. I beg you to be my wife and travel the length and breadth of Ireland with me in my green wagon. Look, here it is under this tree and that's my old horse, Nora, and there's my good dog.'

He stopped because he had no more breath left, and because when he did get his breath back, he was rendered speechless by the beautiful green eyes of the goose maiden, who looked back at him fearlessly even though he was holding her arm.

'Human being,' said she in a low, musical voice, 'I don't think you realize who we are. We are the fairies of the lake who fly around in the shape of geese as it is the most convenient way to travel. I must tell you that there could never be any sort of liaison between a mortal such as yourself and one of us.'

'Oh, most fascinating creature! Oh lovely, fairy princess,' said he, the words jumping off his tongue. 'Give me a chance and I'll promise to make you the happiest Romany wife in the whole of Ireland, with everything that it is in my power to give. What with that and your own magic, we should want for nothing, surely?'

The fairy smiled — a breathtaking sight for Mike — and her green eyes seemed to be kinder as she said, 'Well, I might try it, and it would be a pleasant change not to be flying about in the guise of a goose all the time. Oh, very well then, but I must say goodbye to my sisters and explain everything to them.'

She did so, and when they had all changed into birds again and flown off, she put her hand on Mike's arm and said to him in her enchanting voice, 'Now take me to the green wagon and show me all that you have inside, and I will come and be your wife and live with you, and we will go over all the face of Ireland as you have promised.'

'I will love you forever and a day,' cried Mike joyfully. Lifting her up, he carried her into the caravan and began looking out some clothes for her from his cupboard for, as you will have realised, the bird-lady was as naked as the day she was born.

Mike managed to find for her a long, red silk skirt and a fine embroidered blouse that had been his mother's when she was a bride. Around her shoulders he placed his grandmother's shawl and on her finger went his mother's wedding ring, so that at the next Romany encampment they were taken to be married, and they lived there happily for many months.

Up and down the fair face of Ireland they travelled, and Mike was as happy with his new bride as if he had been a king. The bird-lady, whom he had given the name of Lena, seemed as happy as he and she helped him all the time in the ways that Romany wives do. Mike counted himself a lucky man that he had found her and made her his wife. Time and again said he to himself, 'What other man is there in the whole Romany nation that would have the imagination and the cleverness to fall in love with a bird-fairy and manage to marry her in spite of all her protests that it never could be.'

The following year they were blessed with the arrival of a child. Mike was delighted to see that she was as delicate and as beautiful as his wife — an absolute miniature of her. And for a year or two after that, life was as good as it could be.

Then came a day when Mike found himself once more in the place where he had first met the beautiful Lena. As the horse plodded along the shore of the lake, Lena looked out at the placid waters of her old home, and Mike saw her stretching out her fingers to it in mute appeal. Her wide green eyes were filled with a strange light.

'Lena, Lena, don't look like that,' said he pulling her towards him. 'You have never looked like that before. Aren't you happy with me and little Lena? Doesn't our life together seem as happy to you as I promised it would be?'

'Yes, yes, I suppose it has been nice being married to you and all that and being given a little daughter who looks like me. But I have to say,' she said, 'that the moment I saw the lake again I remembered all my sisters and the life we used to have there — the way we used to swim together and how we flew up into the sky. I forgot I was your wife and that I had actually spent all that time with you, travelling the fair face of Ireland in your green wagon. I just wanted to be back with them.'

As she finished speaking, Mike felt he had to hold onto her, for she seemed to be just about to leap out of the caravan into the air.

'Be at peace, my dear,' said he. 'Don't take on so. I know it must be a shock for you to be looking at your old home and remembering your sisters, but aren't you glad that you love me and I love you?'

'Yes,' she said. And then more faintly, 'Yes.' But he did not feel that she meant to agree. With a sinking heart he realised that she was only pretending.

Little Lena clutched at his coat. Looking down at her, he was amazed to see that her fingers were just like the claws of a young goose, and that feathers seemed to be growing on the back of her hands. A beak was forming where his daughter's nose had been and she uttered a strange cry.

Then his wife turned to him too and said, 'Goodbye. Thank you for everything, my dear. We must go.'

With that, she took off her long red silk skirt and her embroidered blouse and rose into the air, changing once more into a beautiful white bird. Little Lena flew beside her, a daintier facsimile of her mother. They flew once around the caravan before they soared upwards to join a great flock of geese that was winging towards them. Then the light grew so bright that they were merged into it and Mike could see them no more.

He often went back to that lake but he never saw the geese again. So in time he married a nice Romany girl who didn't like water and had never learned how to swim, feeling he might be able to keep her for the rest of his days without worrying whether she would fly off some day. And she didn't. And so they lived happily ever after.

The Romany who Talked to Animals

EFORE THE WAR BETWEEN CATS and mice, which made all cats and mice enemies, and before the Man in the Moon went there at all, but lived at the bottom of a well, there was a Romany who was the seventh son of a seventh son, and his name was Erin Smith. When he was nineteen years old his father called him and said, 'Erin, my boy, there be far too many of us Smiths in this part of the country. And if you walk only a few miles away there's nothing but Lees, so I do bid you go to some other part of the country and try to make a living, for I haven't long now and I would like to see you settled with your own caravan before I go.'

He gave Erin his blessing and the young Romany set off. He walked and walked until he came to the caravan of the Lees and he saw the hard time they had making a living. It was almost as bad as where he had left, so he just went on walking till it was night. By then he was so tired that he had to sit down under a tree. Now, being the seventh son of a seventh son and born on Halloween as well, he could understand the language of the birds and the beasts; and up in that tree, there were two crows. One said to the other as they were settling down in the nest for the night, 'Why, I do declare I seem to have laid a pure gold egg today. I must throw it out of the nest tomorrow — it does feel so very cold.'

So Erin Smith waited patiently at the foot of the tree till early next morning. Then he asked the crow if he could have the egg, and she said he could. So he climbed up and thanked the bird, who said that she was only too happy to be of use to him.

He put the golden egg in his pocket and set off for the nearest town. When he got there, he took it to the jewellers and sold it for a goodly sum of money. He bought himself new boots, a suit of clothes, a moleskin waistcoat and a bright silken handkerchief.

With plenty of money still in his pocket, he looked about for something in which to invest. He went into the seedsman's shop and while he was looking around he saw two small mice at a hole in a sack of seeds. One mouse said to the other, 'If anyone was to buy this seed, he would soon be a very rich man, for three heads of wheat will grow on every stalk.'

So he bought the sack of seed, took it upon his back to a farmer and told him the property of the seed and asked for half of the yield. Now the farmer wanted a husband for his daughter, who was a very ugly girl indeed, so he agreed to take the seed and grow it if Erin Smith would marry his daughter. Having over-heard the cock and the hen in the farmyard talking, Erin agreed and moved into the farmhouse.

For what the cock had said to the hen was, 'If anyone was to marry our master's daughter, it wouldn't be for long. She's likely to die of overeating soon, poor fool, for she will stuff herself from morning to night because she's so ugly. And then he could marry our master's niece, who's as pretty as a picture, and quite an heiress into the bargain.'

So, smiling happily, Erin Smith married the fat ugly daughter and it all happened just as the cock had prophesied. Then Erin went and thanked the cock, telling him that he should live to be as old as he liked and he would never ever be put in the pot.

The corn came up just as the mouse had said. There were three heads on every stalk so that, after it was sold, Erin had quite a tidy sum coming to him. What with that and a pretty wife who didn't at all mind living the life of the travelling people, Erin was able to have a really beautiful new caravan made. He spent a good deal of time painting it all over with flowers and, of course, with animals.

When some time had passed and he found he could no longer live in the farmhouse, for the wanderlust was eating at him, he bade the farmer farewell. Then he and his new wife took to the open road with a fine brown pony between the shafts of their beautifully painted new caravan.

They travelled north and they travelled south, they travelled east and they travelled west until one day what did they do but fetch up in the very part of the country where Erin had been born, among all the Smiths again. By now however, they were all much better off. Most of the other sons had left home and brought back rich wives, just the way Erin had done. They had started buying and selling horses and were getting themselves a good reputation in the area. It was a real joy for Erin to meet them again and find how successful they had become. His old father was delighted to see him and gave a great feast in his honour, with dozens of Romanies sitting around in the firelight afterwards, playing the fiddle and singing Romany songs.

Erin was beginning to wonder how long he should stay there, and considering whether he shouldn't go off first thing in the morning, when the old dog at his knee looked up at him and said, 'Master, do settle down here and carry on with breeding horses and having sons of your own, for though you've travelled north and south, east and west, isn't your own part of the country the best?'

Erin patted his dog and agreed. He threw him a piece of meat, and for all I know that's why there are so many Romanies called Smith in the West Country today.

❧ TALES FROM AFGHANISTAN ❧

The Emir's Cook
and the Unforgettable Sneeze

ABDUR RAMAN, KING OF AFGHANISTAN, was very fond of soup. His favourite was a delicious creamy pea soup, which was made on special days when he would invite visitors and friends from all around the country. A tremendous bowl of soup was placed before Abdur Raman himself and he always enjoyed it to the full, blowing upon it and sniffing its delicious aroma.

It happened that one day, he had invited the leaders of many tribes to his palace and was looking forward to enjoying this special pea soup. As the cook placed the steaming bowl before the King, the wretched man sneezed right into it. Now that is a really terrible thing in any country and King Abdur Raman was mightily annoyed, as his favourite soup was completely ruined.

What was going to happen to the cook? In the years before wisdom had come to Abdur Raman, he might have had the man's head removed. But he wished to be seen to be lenient by the chiefs of the many tribes who were present, so he banished him from his kingdom instead. He said, 'You must leave this place forever and never let me see you again. Go now, before I lose my temper.'

Running and falling, stumbling and picking himself up, the cook went home and said to his wife, 'Give me a bundle, put a few things in it. I must leave forever — I have incurred the royal displeasure. I sneezed into the King's soup in front of all his guests and I can never come back to Afghanistan again.'

His wife said, 'Pull yourself together! It will only be for a short while. Don't worry. People will soon forget, and the King will be happy to see you, because you are the only person who can make the soup that he loves so much. Just stay away for a little while. Here's a little money, a clean shirt and another pair of sandals; don't worry, we'll let you know as soon as the King has calmed down. Go and stay with my nephew in such-and-such a place.'

So the cook kissed his wife and baby goodbye and made off as fast as his legs would carry him, away from the wrath of King Abdur Raman.

A few months passed and the cook left the nephew and managed to get another job in a neighbouring kingdom. He became well known for his soups, gravies and pilaus and earned quite a lot of money; his new master was very pleased with him.

Meanwhile his poor wife was living on what money they had buried under the floor. One day she realised that there was very little left. So she sent her nephew to the neighbouring kingdom, to tell her husband that he should return, throw himself in front of King Abdur Raman and beg for mercy. He was to say he had missed his wife and his child, was very sorry, and that he would never sneeze again. The nephew took some time to reach his uncle. When he finally got there he found that the cook was doing very well indeed and didn't really want to come back. So the nephew said, 'Well, could you give me a little money for my aunt? Then I can tell her that you will come as soon as you can; and in the mean time she can provide for herself.'

The cook, who was now making quite a lot of money, sent a few coins to his wife. He said more would follow later and that he would come when he could.

Two years passed, maybe three. Then, at last, the cook began to feel that he wanted to go back to Afghanistan, to see his wife and how his son had grown up and whether his melons and pumpkins were growing as they should. He wanted, too, to ask the King if he could be forgiven and have his old job back. He was getting really tired of the menu that his new master now insisted upon and he was no longer allowed to prepare the delicious pea soup, gravies and pilaus which he liked to make.

He packed his few belongings, took his money and slipped away very quietly in the night. When he got quite near to his old home, he overheard two women talking as they walked along.

'How are you, my dear?' said one.

'Oh, I'm quite all right,' said the other.

'Any news at all?' said the first.

'No, no, not much. The price of pumpkins is this, the spinach costs that and such-and such-a thing has happened. And my daughter has just heard from her nephew who is in such-and-such a place… and so on.'

'Oh yes, is that the nephew who was married three years ago?'

'Yes, that's right.'

'How old is his child?' asked the first old wife.

'Let me think now. How old is his child? Well, he was born on the night that King Abdur Raman's cook sneezed in the pea soup. So he must be about three.'

And they went on their way, talking and nodding their heads.

The cook fell back, his head hung low. Not only was his unforgettable sneeze now the preserve of gossip-mongers across Kabul, but it had entered into the folklore of Afghanistan. With such a thing hanging over his head, how could he ever return home?

The Magnificent Boots

IN THE TOWN OF MAZAR-I-SHARIF, there once lived a poor boot-maker. One day a fat, rich and important merchant came into his shop and ordered a pair of boots. He said that they must be of the finest leather, of such-and-such a size, right up to his knees with saddle-stitching round the tops, and polished so well that he could see his face in them. The boot-maker, who was called Ramadan because he had been born just as the annual days of fasting had ended, took down all the measurements.

The merchant wanted the boots before he set off on a journey, and said that he would send his servant for them in four days' time. The boot-maker, therefore, dropped all the other work he was going to do, and went out to buy the most expensive leather he could find. He paid a lot of money for it, and for new thread as well. He worked far into the night, while his wife called in vain for him to come and sleep. He worked all the next day, making the right boot, sewing the stitching so carefully that it took twice as long to make this one as it usually took him to make a pair.

He polished the new leather till it shone, massaging wax into it, and then rubbing it with a bone, until he could see the reflection of his face in the toe. He worked the next two days on the second boot, in the same way. By the end of four days of back-breaking toil he had the finest pair of boots ever made by human hands. He placed them in his shop window to be collected by the rich man's servant. But all that day passed, and the next, and the boots were still not collected. His wife was plaintively asking him for money for food, so he parcelled up the precious boots and took them to the house of the man who had ordered them.

The boot-maker knocked at the door of the merchant's big house, and asked to see him as the boots were ready, saying that the price was such-and-such a sum. The servant who answered laughed in Ramadan's face, saying insolently, 'My master has been gone these last two days! He won't be back for six months. I am sure he has changed his mind about those boots… He said he was going to China! So, either you can leave the boots here and get paid when he comes back, if he still wants them then, or take them away and sell them to anyone stupid enough to buy boots made for someone else!'

As Ramadan stood there, looking sadly at the servant and clutching the boots, the other man said sharply, 'Well, are you going to leave them or not? Anyway, get on your way, for I have other things to do than to talk to you.' Mutely, Ramadan turned away, and the rich man's servant banged the door shut.

Slowly, the boot-maker retraced his steps, and put the beautiful shiny boots back in the shop window. Maybe they would sell, but he doubted it, for they were far too expensive to be bought by the average man who lived in Mazar-i-Sharif. The people in the streets usually wore sandals, and the poor none at all, while local horsemen had one pair of leather boots of the toughest sort which lasted them for many years. They liked unstained boots for riding, which were soft to the feet, and comfortable to wear.

'Where is the money you said you would be bringing me when you came back from that rich customer?' asked Ramadan's wife as he closed the shop door and came into their living quarters behind the workroom.

'He has gone to China,' Ramadan told her. 'It seems he left earlier than expected, and does not return for six months. I doubt if he will have them even when he comes back, for his servant said he has probably changed his mind.'

'Oh, oh, what shall I do for money for our food?' lamented the poor woman, so Ramadan gave her some coins from his meagre savings. She went off to the bazaar looking mutinous — she had told him several times that he was very stupid.

Wearily, Ramadan ate a handful of dried pine kernels and went back to his workroom to start on the neglected orders.

The days passed, and the handsome pair of boots stood in his shop window. People did not come in to ask the price, for they could see that it would be too high for the average man. By working night and day again, Ramadan somehow managed to make the boots which he needed to sell in order to get his income back to his usual level. That was not a large amount, as he did not charge people as much as he should for the careful work he put into each pair; he was a craftsman who took great pride in what he created, and that was satisfaction enough. Each day he polished the elegant boots in the window, and kept them looking so beautiful that everyone passing stopped to admire his handiwork. But no one offered to pay his price.

Time passed and Ramadan was beginning to forget the loss he had suffered over the boots, when an impecunious-looking, slim young man came into the shop and asked the price of the magnificent boots. Ramadan looked at him and said, 'I am afraid that they might be too expensive for you, my friend, but I will willingly let you put them on, if you wish. Sit here on this bench, and you shall try them.' He took the boots out of the window and handed them to the young man though, by the look of his clothes, there was little chance of him buying them. He was obviously very poor, and was wearing a pair of worn-out sandals. But Ramadan was proud of his handiwork and pleased to show it to anyone, whatever his station, in order to see the look of appreciation on the face of the enquirer.

'Put them on, my friend,' said the boot-maker, 'and walk about in them. These are kings among boots — just feel the softness of the inner soles!' No sooner were they on his feet than the young man walked proudly up and down the small shop, with such assurance and pride that he seemed transformed from the rather impecunious-looking individual he had been when he came through the door.

Ramadan asked, 'Who are you, young sir, and where are you from, that you have such expensive tastes?' and he smiled, for he knew that it was his boots which had so magically improved the appearance of the customer with the worn-out sandals.

At that moment the door of the shop opened, and an impeccably attired middle-aged man entered. Bowing before the tattered young customer, he said, 'Your Highness, I have been looking everywhere for you! You have given us much anxiety at your disappearance, for the other members of the royal party were afraid that something might have happened to you. Pray, allow me to escort you to the carriage, so that we may proceed to the palace where you are to stay this night.'

The boot-maker's mouth dropped open, for he realised from the elderly man's words that his customer was none other than the Amir's son. He did not know what to say when the prince asked, 'How much do these cost?'

'They are extremely comfortable boots,' he continued, 'and I would like to purchase them, my friend, though you seemed to have doubts that I could afford them when I first entered!'

'Your Highness, I do not know… I was not aware that you…' stammered the boot-maker, covered with confusion.

'You did not know that I sometimes go about dressed as a beggar?' said the Prince. 'But how else could I take back to my father information about the state of Afghanistan's ordinary people? Come, take this purse of gold for your excellent boots. I am delighted with them. Thank you for your good workmanship. My father will be pleased to know that there are still men like you who can make boots for the feet of a King's son!'

With that, the young Prince threw a leather purse onto the counter of the little shop, and the elderly courtier hurried him out. A carriage drawn by two white horses was waiting outside and the Prince drove quickly away.

'Fatima! Fatima! Come and hear what has just happened,' called Ramadan, as his wife came back from the bazaar with a basket over her arm. 'Look, I have sold the boots, and you will never guess to whom!' Then he told her the whole story, and poured twenty gold coins into her basket from the leather purse.

Fatima could scarcely believe him, and thought that she must be dreaming. But then they began to laugh and dance, and bless the day that Ramadan had received the order for the expensive boots. 'How mysterious are the workings of Providence,' she murmured, as she counted and re-counted the shining coins. 'This money will be enough to keep us in comfort for a long time You will be able to close the shop for a while soon, so that we can go to visit my mother in the country, before you have to come back and start again. I do not remember when it was that we had a holiday. Never in our lives have we had so much money!'

And so it was that what had seemed at first to be a calamity, was turned into a blessing for the boot-maker. Although the rich merchant who had changed his mind never returned from China, many among those who attended the Prince came to the boot-maker's little shop to order their new boots, because they realised that his workmanship was the finest in all the land.

The Prince who Feared Tigers

ONCE THERE WAS A KING who had a handsome son of whom he was very fond. He had the young prince trained in every form of courtly behaviour, and schooled in mathematics, geometry and astronomy. The prince was also taught how to write poetry, as well as the study of the classic books of ancient times. When he was eighteen years old, the King said to him: 'Iskandar, my son, there is a secret which all princes in our family learn at the age you are now. There is a tiger which has been bred for the purpose and is extremely fierce and strong. It is to be your task to go into its cage, armed only with one dagger and with a small shield. My son, you must fight that tiger, or you will never be King. I was sent into the cage to fight a similar tiger when I was your age, and with the power of my right arm I managed to plunge the dagger into its heart. My father was pleased with me, and announced to the people that I had passed the test of daring and strength which the princes of this family must all undergo, in order to become King.'

Iskandar was distressed at this news and said: 'I have no liking for fighting with beasts, father; let me wrestle a man, or even an *afreet*, but a tiger… why, it sounds impossible to me.'

The King looked displeased and said, 'Unless you pass this test, how are the people ever going to accept you as their King after I am dead? Come, come, now, it is not so hard a task; a strong young man like you should be able to dispose of such a beast easily. You need courage, that is all. If you lack the courage to fight the tiger, then I am afraid you will be considered a coward.'

Iskandar was terrified by the very idea, but replied, 'Let me see the animal, father, and then tell me when it is that I am expected to fight it.'

'Of course,' replied the King. 'I will show it to you now, and you may decide when you feel prepared to go into the cage with it, in order to dispatch it. That should be within the next few days, I suppose.'

He led the trembling young prince to a deep dungeon under the castle where, in an iron cage, a fierce-looking tiger with huge teeth and a vicious snarl was chewing at a large bone.

'Did it take you long to kill yours, father?' asked Iskandar faintly, as he wondered what it would be like to be in the cage with the savage beast. 'Oh, no, not long,' replied his father softly. 'I knew where to thrust the knife, and I pleased your grandfather very much by the speed with which I finished it off.'

Iskandar could not get out of the dungeon quickly enough. As he followed the King up into the fresh air of the palace courtyard his mind was in turmoil. How could he avoid such a dreadful confrontation, which his father seemed to think was such an easy matter?

He promised to tell his father as soon as he was ready for the ordeal, and hurried to his own room. Physically, he knew he was strong enough but, at that moment, he just felt overwhelmingly afraid. What was he to do?

At dinner that night he was subdued, wrestling with the problem. But soon after he went to bed his mind was made up: he would leave the palace as soon as his parents were asleep and probably never return. He could not persuade himself that he could fight and kill the tiger.

At midnight he rose, dressed in very ordinary clothes, and

made his way to the stable, taking a small bag of gold concealed in his belt for emergencies. He asked a sleepy groom to saddle his favourite horse and he rode away from his home. He had not even left a note for his father, so ashamed was he of his cowardice.

He pointed his horse's head in a northerly direction and, by morning, he had arrived at a pleasant river with flowery meadows on either bank. Here he dismounted to let his horse drink, and crop at the sweet grass. Presently, he heard the sound of a shepherd boy playing upon a pipe, and then saw him leading a small flock of sheep to pasture. Iskandar asked the boy if there was somewhere he might stay for a few days. The boy pointed to a road leading up to a large house where his master lived, saying that he was always happy to welcome strangers, and was very generous and hospitable.

The master of the house, who also owned much of the surrounding lands, made Iskandar welcome when he arrived and invited him to stay for as long as he wished. After they had breakfasted together, he asked Iskandar, 'From whence do you come and whither are you going?' Iskandar answered evasively, 'I have troubles at home which have forced me to leave for a while. For the time being, I must ask you not to press me for details; I am seeking the answer to my problem by myself.'

The older man then replied that he quite understood, and said, 'Please stay here as long as you wish, and treat this house as your own: in time, no doubt, the answer to your problem will be suggested to you by Providence.' The prince's horse was led away and stabled. After walking in the gardens by himself for a while, Iskandar felt he would like to stay in these tranquil surroundings until his problem solved itself. His only thought was that he did not want to return home.

Each day he discovered some new and enchanting spot where he could enjoy the river and hear the shepherds playing on their pipes; or he would ride his horse to vantage points from which he could view the surrounding countryside, and admire the trees and abundant grapes which grew on terraced vines on every side.

One night, as he looked out of his bedroom window, he saw to his horror that there was a tiger in the grounds. As he heard the snarling of the ferocious beast, his heart stood still and the blood froze in his veins. That night he tossed and turned, unable to sleep. Next morning his host asked him: 'Did you sleep well? You do not look very rested.'

'No, I couldn't sleep,' said Iskandar. 'I saw a large tiger in the grounds, and I heard it snarling — it seems to be quite a dangerous creature. Do you often have them here… so near the house, I mean?'

'Oh, yes, there are quite a few hereabouts,' replied the land-owner. 'We scarcely notice them, and of course everything is very securely guarded after dark. My night-watchmen are instructed to shoot them on sight if they go near the stables or the sheep-pens.' He did not seem the slightest bit alarmed by the fact that Iskandar had seen a tiger, and smiled most amiably as he was speaking. That afternoon, as soon as he could get his horse saddled, Iskandar bade goodbye to his generous host, and set off on his journey north once more — this news about the local tigers had quite unsettled him.

He rode on until nightfall, and he was happy to see a large fort, and several men with guns standing on guard outside the main gate. As night was falling, they were preparing to secure the gates for the greater security of those inside. Iskandar dismounted and told them he was a traveller seeking shelter for the hours of darkness; so for a gold coin he was allowed in, and his horse was given hay and bedded down. As they sat round a tray heaped with spiced rice and mutton, the owner of the fort, a tall bearded warrior, politely asked him, 'Where are you from, and whither are you going?'

'Please do not ask me,' pleaded Iskandar. 'Suffice it to say that I am one who has had to leave home with a difficult problem which I must solve by myself, with no help from anyone.'

The bearded warrior nodded his head, and stroked his beard as he ate with Iskandar from the tray. After a cup of delicious green tea, a servant took the young man to the guest chamber and the warrior climbed the stairs to his own apartments, saying to Iskandar as he left, 'May your night be blessed, and remember: Time gives us all the answers.'

Next day he asked the prince to go hawking with him and his companions, which Iskandar did with much enjoyment, delighting in the fresh air and wild scenery. After a wonderful day of sport they returned to a grand feast, where the whole party ate and drank together in warm companionship. As they were about to go to bed, the warrior said to Iskandar, 'My men and I have been pleased with your company today, and have admired the way in which you have entered into the spirit of our simple sport. These warriors of mine and I are all seasoned campaigners — we frequently have to fight other tribes to avenge blood feuds or for other reasons.'

'Great personal bravery is then required to ensure the survival of our own tribe. There is another sport in which we indulge, which is a good test of our bravery and proficiency in these warlike skills,' he continued. 'We want to invite you to take part and test your own prowess. Two miles to the south of here is an area which is infested with tigers. We usually rise and perform the dawn prayer; then, beseeching Allah to protect us, we go out to do battle with those tigers. We take spear, dagger and shield, and usually get at least one of the fierce creatures. We would be very happy if you could accompany us tomorrow.' Then he said he hoped the guest would sleep soundly, as the next day would be tiring.

Iskandar's face paled as he said goodnight. He scarcely slept until dawn and then he rode his horse out into the pearly sunrise. He knew that he could not join those fearsome warriors in their tiger hunt, so as soon as he was not being watched by the others he urged his horse in another direction, and this time he galloped westwards as fast as his gallant mare could carry him.

'I cannot understand it,' he said to himself. 'Why is it that there are tigers wherever I go? Did I not even leave home in order to avoid confrontation with one of them?'

He rode on, until at last he came to a charming region of hills and dales covered with small fruit trees and shrubs with sweet-smelling blossoms. He got down from the saddle to stretch his legs and let his horse drink from a tranquil pool. Then, riding on, he saw a wonderful palace, finer than any he had known before. It was of rose-coloured stone, with pillars set with mosaics of sky-blue tiles, and balconies of painted wood carved with delicate designs. There were fountains of pure water in the gardens all around the palace, and pavilions where sweetly singing birds had their nests.

'This is surely a Paradise on Earth!' said Iskandar to himself, and approached the palace quite timidly, half-expecting it to belong to some *peri*, or fairy being, who would cause it to disappear as soon as he got nearer. But a guard standing at the main gate saluted him and a boy came to lead his horse away to the stables as if he were an honoured and expected guest. Iskandar was then taken to a guest room by another servant, who showed him where he could bathe and change into clothes laid out for him on a couch.

Asking the servants the name of the owner of such a fine palace, he learned that their master was the King's Prime Minister, who was at that moment with his beloved only daughter, Bibi Maryam, and that she was the most beautiful young lady in the land.

As soon as he was dressed, a servant came to request Iskandar's presence at a meal with the minister; soon they were sitting together, eating a huge dinner of venison and spiced rice.

'Where are you from, and where are you going?' asked the host, as they finished the meal with fresh apricots and melons, pistachio nuts and almonds.

My situation is such that I cannot talk about it,' stammered Iskandar. 'I have had to leave home because of a problem which I feel I cannot yet face. I hope you will forgive me if I repeat that I would rather say no more.'

'I understand,' nodded the minister, stroking his beard, and giving the young man a pat on the shoulder. 'Have some green tea with cardamom in it, and tell me all about it tomorrow, if you wish.' Then, when it was time for sleep, he led Iskandar to a guest room with a huge carved bed, and told him he was welcome to stay in the palace for as long as he wished.

Left to himself beside the fire of blazing pine branches which blazed in the grate, Iskandar told himself that here at last was one place where he would like to stay for a long time. It reminded him of his home, and he shed a few tears as he remembered that he had left his father without a word, maybe forever. He knew now that he was a coward indeed.

Several days passed before one afternoon he saw Bibi Maryam, the Prime Minister's beautiful daughter, for the first time. She was sitting in the garden, singing to herself in a charming and pleasant voice, accompanying herself on a delicate stringed instrument. Just as he was about to go forward and introduce himself to her, he froze in his tracks. Beside her, lying on the grass at her feet, was a large and very aggressive-looking tiger. The lady looked in his direction and said, 'So you are our guest this week? I have seen you several times, eating with my father. We can look at who is in the banqueting hall below when we lean over the balcony from the harem,' and she gave a delicious giggle. The tiger raised its head and looked at Iskandar with huge green eyes, bright as emeralds. Its teeth looked very sharp, and he backed away. 'I'm … I'm sorry to have disturbed you,' he said faintly. 'I must go now. I am sure that I should not have interrupted you at your music.' He would have liked to turn and run, but he was afraid that the tiger would chase him if he did.

'Oh, nonsense,' said she. 'Please come over here and sit down. My father has just told me I should entertain you and introduce my lovely pet tiger to you. Come, be seated, please, in that chair,' and she indicated a seat opposite her. With every nerve in his body tingling with anxiety, Iskandar forced himself to sit where she pointed. He looked rather shyly at her and inwardly agreed that she must indeed be the most beautiful lady in the land. He had never seen anyone so lovely. Her eyes were large and dark, fringed with black lashes and she had a full, rose-pink mouth. Her copper-coloured hair gleamed and she wore a leaf-green robe. As she began to sing again the tiger closed its eyes and lay down beside her, purring like a domestic cat. Iskandar felt a little bit braver, now that the animal's gaze was not fixed on his face. Bibi Maryam was as delicate a being as he had ever seen and he felt himself falling in love with her. But how could she ever feel anything for a coward like himself, he wondered bitterly.

The Prime Minister and his wife came into the garden to sit with their daughter and Iskandar, and they all drank many cups of sweetened green tea. Her parents seemed pleased to see the young people becoming so friendly, though now and again the prince could not stop himself casting rather anxious glances towards the tiger on the grass at Bibi Maryam's feet. After they had enjoyed more of Bibi Maryam's music, they went inside and the minister said to Iskandar, 'By the way, do not be alarmed if the tiger should come snuffling at your bedroom door in the night. When we have all retired to bed, he likes to patrol the corridors to be sure that there are no thieves about!' and he laughed, seeming not to notice that Iskandar had gone as pale as milk.

Sure enough, that night when all was still, Iskandar heard the tiger snuffling at his door and making the handle rattle with its claws. He lay in bed, petrified with fear. Again he could not go to sleep, although he knew that the door was locked. In the morning, before opening the door, he took out the key and peered through the keyhole. The tiger was gone.

Then and there, Iskandar made up his mind to return home. With so many tigers to be dealt with everywhere, surely the one at home in his father's dungeon could scarcely be much trouble? As soon as he was washed and dressed he went to the minister, and said, 'I ask your permission to leave your palace. I wish to return to my home because I am now resolved to face the problem which I left behind. If I do not, I shall never find peace, however far away I go. I am the son of a King, and I have been a coward, but I want to return and change all that so that my family name will not be dishonoured. I am deeply ashamed and I know that, unless I succeed, I can never ask for the hand in marriage of a lady like your daughter Bibi Maryam, whom I love dearly. She herself is so brave, she has a tiger for a pet! I am not afraid any more, and I will face my fate at home, whatever it may be…'

'Well spoken, Prince Iskandar,' replied the minister. 'I knew who you were as soon as you came, because you so closely resemble your father when he was your age. Go, kill the tiger, and I will give you my beloved Bibi Maryam with great pleasure, if she be willing. Allah's blessing upon you both!'

So Iskandar rode off as fast as his horse would carry him, towards his home. When he passed the fort of the bearded warrior, who should be standing outside but the old man himself. The prince pulled up, then dismounted and spent the night there. As he was leaving, the warrior said, 'I knew who you were, Prince Iskandar because you are the image of your respected father, for whom I had the honour to fight in many battles in bygone days, before you were born. You are the same as he was at your age. I am glad that you are returning to him, for you are your father's only son and your duty is to return and fight the tiger.' Then he gave the young prince his blessing, and saw him on his way.

Well-rested, Iskandar rode on until he arrived at the pleasant, flowery meadows where he had first heard the music of the simple shepherd boy playing upon his pipe, leading the flock of sheep to pasture. He recollected the generous hospitality of the owner of those lands, and rode up to enquire if the good man was at home. The doorman replied that indeed the master was within, and announced Iskandar's arrival. Iskandar was immediately made just as welcome as he had been before.

After eating with his host, Iskandar told him that the problem which had so perplexed him on his first visit was now resolved, and he was on his way home. 'To slay the tiger, I hope?' said the landowner, with a smile. 'That is a good decision, for your father would have been heart-broken if you had not followed the family tradition.'

Iskandar was amazed and said: 'Then you, too, know my father and the tradition that each son must overthrow the tiger before he can be accepted as the true successor?'

'Yes,' was the answer. 'I knew who you were when first I saw you. You are the very image of your respected father when he was your age, and I realised what must have been troubling you before. Allah's blessing be upon you, Prince Iskandar, and may you be successful in the test which lies before you.' Then they parted company, and Iskandar spurred his horse to greater efforts, so eager was he now to get to his contest with the tiger. He thought about his beautiful and beloved Bibi Maryam constantly, and the courage he needed came to his heart as he drew nearer to his home.

Arriving at the palace, Iskandar kissed his father's hand and begged the King's forgiveness for running away from his destiny in such a manner. 'Now let me go to the tiger with dagger and shield, as soon as is possible,' he continued, 'for I am ready for the test.'

'Excellent,' said the King, and turning to the nearest courtier he commanded, 'see to it that the Prince is given suitable protection for his body and the best dagger and shield in the armoury, so that he may face the tiger as soon as possible. If

Allah wills, he will kill it and so qualify for the throne of this land after me.'

Excitement swept through the entire palace then, so that when Iskandar was taken to the dungeon where the tiger was confined, all cheered him on his way below. The keeper of the fearsome beast unbolted the iron door of the cage and the animal snarled, showing its gleaming white teeth. With the dagger in his right hand and the small shield in his left, Iskandar went bravely into the cage. For a moment his heart seemed to stop beating, but he stepped forward, his strength returning, and lifted the blade to plunge it into the animal's throat. Suddenly, to his astonishment, the giant creature began to purr and rubbed its head against his knees, licking his boots like a pet hound. The keeper of the tiger took the dagger from the young man's hand and said, 'See, auspicious Prince, this animal is as tame as a pet cat! It has never injured any human in its life. In fact, it has been bred and trained in order to test your courage, and by Divine Providence your true valour has been proved today!'

Iskandar laughed heartily, so great was his relief at the turn of events, and with the huge animal following at his heels, he went to his father with an easy heart. 'So,' smiled the King, 'you now know how the test of the tiger is carried out by each generation, from prince to prince, until today it was your turn! I am proud of you, my son, you are a worthy successor to my crown.' And he embraced him with great joy. The tiger lay down beside them, gazing at Iskandar with its large green eyes, perfectly at ease among the courtiers now coming forward to congratulate their prince on his success.

Iskandar lost no time in sending a fast-riding messenger to Bibi Maryam, to tell her that now he felt she would not think him a coward, and asking her to come and marry him, when her father was willing.

After he received the answer he was seeking, it seemed an eternity before his bride-to-be arrived with her cavalcade of relatives and servants, bringing presents of great price, as befitted a lady of such quality who was to become his princess. The wedding festivities went on for fourteen days and fourteen nights, and many coins were thrown daily to the poor from the palace balcony. Gallons of green tea were quaffed in the tea-houses by the entire populace, and all hearts were happy at the marriage of their young prince and his princess. The tiger which Bibi Maryam brought with her to her new home played most amicably with the one which was now Iskandar's pet, and they followed their master and mistress like tame cats for all the rest of their lives.

The Pebble which Wanted
to Travel the World

ONCE UPON A TIME, by the side of a river, there was a small, smooth pebble. It lay beside a pile of grey rocks, which could be heard boasting to each other about how far they had come.

'I am from the very top of the mountains,' cried one. 'Yes, I am in fact part of the High Pamir Mountain Range, for I fell and rolled and finally landed here, at this spot, many thousands of years ago.'

'Yes,' said another, close by, 'I too came from far up in the mountains; my head was piercing the clouds, right up there in the sky. One day a huge landslide brought me down, so fast that I knew nothing until I landed here by the river. I must be even older than you. What a wonderful thing it is for remarkable rocks like us to tell of the story of our noble creation!'

'Once I must have been part of a rock too,' said the very small and insignificant pebble. 'I must be extremely old also, for look how smooth and worn my body is, as shiny and round as is the gigantic moon. What fun it would be if I could jump up from where I have lain so long, and go travelling to the very end of the world!'

'Silence, stupid pebble, show respect for your elders,' said the first rock. 'How could something as insignificant and ignorant as you go out into the world? Do you know how large it is?'

'No,' replied the pebble, 'but I would like to find out.'

The old grey rocks laughed so loudly that they shamed the pebble into closing his tiny mouth, and he entered no more into the high-flown conversation of his superiors. But the thoughts went on, until the desire to travel became an obsession, and one day the pebble had an idea. The next time a camel caravan passed that way, laden with sacks of mulberries for the nearest town, he got between the toes of a huge Bactrian camel's left hind foot, and stuck there for a long time. When the caravan had gone several miles, the cameleer noticed that the camel was limping. He examined its feet, removed the pebble and threw it away with a curse. The slow, lumbering line of camels passed on, their brass bells jingling round their necks.

The pebble now found himself near a small house in which there lived an ancient dervish. The old man had put his shoes outside the door, as he always did before entering his humble abode, and the pebble made a leap from where the camel-driver had thrown it and managed to land in one of them. Next time the dervish wanted to go on a journey the pebble travelled with him, cleverly hidden inside the toe of the shoe. The day was hot and the road was dusty; after a few miles, the pebble began to hurt the dervish's foot. Sitting down on a stump of a fallen tree, the dervish muttered to himself, 'Have I got a blister, that my shoe hurts me so much?' and took off the offending shoe. He felt his foot, and then put his fingers into the toe and extracted the pebble. 'Ahah! So that is what was hurting…well, that's not going to trouble me any more!' and he threw it into the river.

As luck would have it, the pebble fell right into the mouth of a very big fish which was just opening its jaws to snap at a fly, and was swallowed in a trice. He lay in the darkness of the fish's stomach, very frightened, wishing that he had never decided to go on a journey and leave that place of safety beside the sheltering rocks. He could not imagine what had happened; it was as if all the daylight had gone from the world.

How long the pebble remained in the fish's stomach is not known, but one day the fish was caught by a man with a net, who took it home in triumph to feed his family that night. When his wife was cleaning the fish before she put it into the pot, she found the pebble. Holding it up to the light, she said to her husband, 'Look what I have just taken out of the fish's stomach, my dear! It has such a pretty shape — I will wash it and have it made into a ring. Look, is that not the most beautiful colour?' The fisherman agreed with her, for in the light, the pebble looked very suitable for setting in a ring, being smooth, round and brightly coloured, the size of a small pea.

The next time they went to the town, the fisherman's wife took the pebble tied in a corner of her headscarf, and while her husband was selling his fish she visited the jeweller in the bazaar. 'How much would it cost to make this into a ring, please?' she asked. 'Do not expect me to pay a lot for it, for I am only a poor woman.' The jeweller put a glass into his eye and examined the pebble carefully.

He realised that this was a stone which would fetch a good price if it were to be set in silver and offered to a certain noble-man. So he said to the woman, 'I am not sure if I could make you a suitable ring from such a stone, but if you give it to me, I will offer you in exchange this turquoise ring which I made only last week, and which I think will fit your finger perfectly.' He slipped the blue turquoise ring into her hand, and the woman put it on. The ring fitted the middle finger of her right hand perfectly. She smiled with satisfaction and went away, rejoicing that she had got such a good bargain.

The pebble soon found himself on the jeweller's bench with a silver collar round his middle. That was then attached to a heavy silver ring. 'What has happened to me?' he asked himself, for he was now weighed down by the silver and could not hop off the jeweller's bench. He wanted to get away from the noisy bazaar where there was so much clamour, and such unfamiliar stress. The situation was not to the pebble's liking for he was now a prisoner, no longer free to go to the end of the world as he had planned.

Having finished the job of making the pebble into a ring to show the nobleman, the jeweller was well pleased with himself, and putting the ring into a small leather pouch, he set off for the nobleman's house. The pebble was once more in darkness and also in great despair. This must be the end. How he wished he were back, lying by the riverside and safe in the shadow of the old grey rocks at the foot of the great mountains.

The jeweller arrived at his destination, and soon the ring was being admired by the purchaser. The jeweller asked and was given ten times the worth of the turquoise ring he had given in exchange for the pebble to the fisherman's wife.

So, although the humans were all satisfied, the unhappy pebble was in great distress. Here he was, fixed to this dreadful ring, being moved from box to box in the nobleman's treasury, sometimes taken out, examined, and gloated over, at other times passed around from hand to hand in admiration. He was plunged into the depths of despair. He would never be able to escape now.

How long he remained in that condition, he did not know. But one day things took a surprising turn for the better. In the nobleman's household there was a bad servant who was dismissed by his master for his dishonest ways. When he left he stole a box of rings, among which was the one set with the pebble. The thief went to the receiver of stolen goods to whom he usually sold his ill-gotten gains, and that villain prised the silver from the pebble in order to sell the precious metal to a jeweller as scrap.

As soon as he was free again, the pebble rejoiced, but he was not yet completely free, for the villain then put the pebble into his waistcoat pocket, thinking to sell it somewhere else. One day, as the man's wife was shaking the dust from the waistcoat, the pebble fell out of the pocket and through the window, right into a busy street. Down below, a young man was pushing a barrow laden with baskets of dried peas which he was going to sell in the bazaar. He called his wares in a loud voice: 'Dried peas! Dried peas! Come buy, buy!'

What was to happen next? Listen, and I will tell you.

That very day a maidservant had been sent by her mistress to purchase a bag of dried peas, and another of beans for the next day's meal. The pebble fell into the middle of a basket of wrinkled dried peas, and when the young man weighed the purchase for the girl, she did not notice the pebble there — she was admiring the barrow-boy's good looks. Back to her mistress's house she ran, as fast as she could go, for she had been dawdling in the bazaar. Her mistress was already calling to her to put the bags in the larder and cut the aubergines for the master's midday meal.

That evening, the beans and peas were put into different bowls of water to soak all night. Next day, the mistress cooked the meal with peas, onions and rice, her husband's favourite dish, but the master of the house spat out his first mouthful and shouted: 'What is the meaning of this stone in the stew, wife? Did you not wash the dried peas and beans before you put them in to soak? I nearly broke a tooth on this!' The pebble rolled away across the floor and his wife pacified him as best she could. No more pieces of stone were found in the rest of the dish and tranquillity was soon restored.

But what of the unfortunate pebble? He lay under the table all night, and in the morning he was swept out into the garden by the maid with the rest of the dust and rubbish. At about midday, the gardener came and began building a new rockery for the lady, who wanted one made from a lot of stones which were lying about near the rose bushes. He spied the pebble and placed it on top of a pile of coloured stones to make a pretty arrangement. All round the pebble, the gardener put good brown earth and carefully placed flowering plants of the sort seen naturally in rocky crevices high on the mountainside. He watered the rock-garden carefully for days; the sun came out and everything round the pebble grew in delightful profusion. The young daughters of the house often came to admire the gardener's art, and all enjoyed the scent of the flowers, including the pebble. He looked up from his shelter of tiny blossoms, and was glad that their tender green leaves protected him from the noonday sun. The garden was peaceful, and the water of the fountain beside the rose-bower tinkled like the mountain stream of his old home. At night, he saw the stars and watched the moon grow from her maidenhood of a thin silver crescent in the black velvet sky, to a round plump queen of beauty when she was full. He was content.

'No more going to the end of the world for me,' he said to himself. 'Enough of wandering, of being trodden by camels, and being imprisoned, and stolen, and swallowed by a fish, hidden in a dervish's shoe, thrown out of a window, or cooked in a stew!

Why, the peace of this flowery rock-garden is all that I shall ever need. I'm away from the shadow of those cantankerous old grey rocks, who looked down on me, and called me ignorant and stupid. All they ever did was to fall to the bottom of the hill. I shall never go back there and be subservient to them again. I have my own small mountain here and I am on the very top of it, among the flowers, regularly looked after by the kindly old gardener. My wanderings are over. If the rest of the world is like the part that I have seen, I don't want to experience any more such horrors, and that is my whole-hearted decision.'

With that, he snuggled closer to the soft brown earth and went to sleep in a tiny crevice. And for all I know, he is there to this day. There is a perfect place for everything in this world, and the pebble had found his at last.

The Lost Mares

ONCE THERE LIVED A MAN called Akbar Khan, who bred the finest horses in Afghanistan. He loved horses more than any living things, and his name was known from north to south, and east to west. His mares were fat and sleek, his foals were bought by the Amir's Horse Master, and his black stallion, Siahpoosh, was as dear to him as a son.

One night when Akbar was asleep, sleeping the deep sleep of one who has nothing to fear, thieves crept silently into his stables and stole three of his best mares.

As soon as he discovered they were gone, Akbar left the stables in charge of his old groom and set out on his stallion to find them.

'Even if I have to ride to the ends of the Earth, I shall find them and bring them back!' vowed Akbar Khan. 'May you never grow tired!' called the old groom as he rode away.

Soon he picked up their trail in the dust, and felt a fierce joy. He prayed to The Compassionate that he would find them quickly, but the thieves had driven the horses fast and he rode through many a village and farming area without catching up with them. At one village, he was told that he had just missed two men with five horses, heading towards a large town. Akbar Khan knew that the horse sales held there every year were soon to take place. As he approached the town, he tied the great stallion to a tree near the river. He knew that no one would dare to steal his horse for fear of those lashing hooves and wicked teeth, for Siahpoosh would allow no man to ride him but Akbar Khan.

'Assuredly I will find them here,' said Akbar Khan to himself, and sauntered into a tea-house. There he quaffed several cups of green tea, looking round for someone he knew. 'If such there be in this place,' he thought to himself, 'he will help me, for to an Afghan, the stealing of mares is the most dreadful of crimes.'

At that moment, an old friend sat down beside him and Akbar Khan told him why he had come. 'Unfortunately, I lost track of their hoof-prints some way back,' said Akbar Khan, 'but this seems to be the best place to renew the search.

'Can you tell me when the sales take place? — I have a feeling the rogues will try to sell the mares soon.'

'Two strangers came into town last night,' confided the other, 'and yes, they had three very fine mares with them, though they rode horses of a lower grade than those you breed, O my brother.'

'Where did they go? Have they put them in stables?' asked Akbar Khan.

'We can search the various stables where horses are kept until the sales and we can look for them there,' answered the man, 'but I fear that they may have hidden them somewhere to forestall discovery until the actual sales are in progress. They begin tomorrow.'

'I have a plan. I will bring Siahpoosh into the town and he will find them. Let us go to where I have tied him and we will see what he can do,' said Akbar Khan. 'By Allah, I will not wait until tomorrow!'

So they returned to the river bank and Akbar Khan spoke into the huge stallion's ear.

What he said, the other man did not hear, nor was it meant that he should. The black horse understood every word that his master spoke: his ears pricked up, and he gave a mighty neigh as Akbar Khan finished. Then his master leapt into the saddle, turned the stallion's head, and began to ride back slowly. As they neared the town, the horse began to trot and soon Akbar's friend was left behind. The people who saw horse and rider approaching made way for them to pass, for the sight of that wonderful horse was a joy to behold in a town where fine horses were so highly prized.

They went right through the town. Then, as they approached a wooden fence surrounding a stable yard, the stallion threw up his head, once, twice, and gave a loud cry. Siahpoosh stopped dead, and whinnied again. He pawed the ground with his right foreleg, like a military charger hearing the sound of battle. Then he pawed the earth with his left foreleg, and Akbar Khan knew that he had found the place where his mares were imprisoned. When he heard them whinny in reply, he turned Siahpoosh about and gave the order to kick. The iron hooves lashed out and splintered the flimsy wood until the whole stable door was demolished. The mares whinnied again as Akbar Khan freed them, one by one, from the hooks to which they had been tethered.

Two men came running out to see what was happening, and they felt the stinging lash of the rope's end with which Akbar Khan thrashed them; they fled, howling like dogs. Akbar led his horses to the river and let them drink. The townsfolk gathered around him, for by now his friend had caught up and told onlookers the story of the stolen mares. Everyone was eager to offer Akbar Khan hospitality until he was ready to take the road home again. When the young men of the town went to look for them, the two horse-thieves were nowhere to be found, which was lucky for them for they would have been thrashed even more severely than by Akbar Khan. But everyone knew that retribution would one day come to those who steal horses, and called them thrice-cursed, for in Afghanistan the theft of a mare is a most grievous crime.

Akbar Khan returned to his own territory of the God-given Kingdom, to live out the rest of his days in happiness and good fortune, until the Terminator of Delights on Earth sent him to Paradise at last.

The Precious Pearl

BABAR SHAH, KING OF AFGHANISTAN and conqueror of Hindustan, was sitting writing in his diary one day, when a minister entered, and said: 'There awaits a representative of the Sheikh of Bahrain, O King, with a valuable present from that Land of Pearls. When will you see him?'

'Cause him to be admitted at once,' replied Babar Shah without ceremony, laying aside his writing, 'and bring food for us to eat here together, and sweet sherbet made with mulberry juice and snow, that he should be refreshed from his journey.'

Several hours later, when the Arab had been feasted, and given presents of lapis-lazuli ornaments, he placed in Babar Shah's hand a magnificent pearl — a pearl beyond price, saying, 'My master begs your Majesty to accept this small token of his esteem, as a sign of his respect and friendship.'

The pearl was one of the finest the King had ever seen, and he was delighted with the gift. He heaped even more presents upon the Arab and sent him on his way rejoicing, after several more days of hospitality.

Now Babar Shah's Queen was very jealous of this present which had been given to her husband, for she dearly loved jewellery, and she loved pearls above all other gems. She began to wonder how she could acquire it for herself. But the King wanted the pearl fixed onto a pin, so that he could wear it himself — he felt it had a certain fortunate quality about it, having come at a time when his diary was going particularly well, his gardeners were getting on wonderfully with the new gardens he had designed, and news concerning his army was as good as he could possibly hope.

The Queen had everything in the world that a queen could desire. She knew that her husband looked on her with great favour; her robes and jewels were the talk of the Court: yet above all things she desired the King's pearl. She lay at night planning how she would have it set, not in plain gold as her husband planned, but in a wonderful ring surrounded with turquoises and red rubies from Badakhshan. Everyone would notice it and she would be the envy of all. Night after night, she tossed and turned. Soon she looked quite ill and thin, so much so that Babar Shah grew worried about her state of health.

He said to her gently, 'What unusually flushed cheeks you have just lately, my dear one. Do you feel unwell? Is it a fever? Tell me, for I am anxious about you, my rose-bodied one. Is there anything that ails you?'

'No, no, I am not sleeping well because I have been eating too many sweetmeats made by my old nurse. That is why I am not quite myself these last few days. I will stop eating so much halwa and Turkish delight. I am afraid it is my own greed!'

Babar Shah kissed her on the brow and went out of the harem to attend to affairs of State, and soon he had immersed himself in his official papers.

Now, the Queen had a clever slave who was as sly as a vixen. She asked her in confidence to think how she might possess herself of the King's pearl without arousing the King's anger.

'I know a way, my lady,' simpered the slave. 'You should ask the Court Physician to prescribe a crushed pearl, of the same shape and size as the pearl of Bahrain, as the only cure for your malady. A few gold coins will induce him to prescribe this, and the King will not deny you the medicine.'

'Zamena,' cried the Queen delightedly, 'you are a clever creature! Bring the harem physician here at once and also a purse of gold. He is a silly old fellow — I brought him with me from my father's house when I married the King. so of course he will obey me! I can pretend to crush the pearl in my pestle and mortar, and swallow the glass of milk into which I shall say that I have stirred the powdered pearl.'

Laughing, the slave Zamena ran off, but she had a twin brother to whom she confided the plot. That boy was one of the King's pages and fiercely loyal to Babar Shah so he told the King the whole story. Upon hearing of his wife's plan, Babar Shah shouted with laughter and, slapping his thigh, said, 'This is a great jest! You can never keep up with the wiles of women, whether you be a slave or a King! Keep this secret and tell no one, for I shall have a part in this as well.'

The aged, grey-bearded physician duly came to request the pearl of Bahrain from his Majesty, which he swore was the only thing that would cure the Queen's malady. Babar Shah agreed, and taking the pearl from his pocket, removed it from the piece of silken cloth in which it was wrapped, saying, 'Why, of course you must take this and make the medicine for my beloved lady. I will deny her nothing, good doctor. But wait! Instead of you having the trouble of rendering it to a powder, I will do that myself. I am not unskilled in the apothecary's art, you know. Go, bring the finest marble pestle and mortar you can find.'

The King sat down to await the carrying out of his order, smoothing his beard with a careful hand to hide the smile upon his lips.

From behind the carved screens of the harem, the Queen

watched what was going on with dismay. She knew that she was going to lose the pearl just as it was within her grasp. She reached out with a gold-embroidered slipper to beat the slave Zamena who had suggested this foolish plan, and bit her royal lips. What could she do to save the pearl from destruction? She saw the doddering old physician return with the pestle and mortar, saw the firm strong fingers of Babar Shah throw something white and shining into the marble bowl, saw her husband's steady preoccupation with what he was doing, inexorably grinding, grinding the pearl to powder. At last it was done to the King's satisfaction, and he called for a crystal goblet into which he threw the powder, pouring in the milk, then stirring it slowly. He sent a servant to bring the royal lady to him, and with his own hand placed it before her.

'Now, drink, my dear one, and may your health improve soon, with Allah's help.' He smiled as the Queen swallowed the mixture with half a smile and half a sob. Then, without raising her eyes, she went slowly back to the harem.

When an hour had passed, Babar Shah went to her. She was lying on her bed, pale and sad, and he raised her cold hands to his lips. 'Your hot cheeks are pale as lilies again, my love — the medicine has chased away your fever very quickly,' he said softly. She moaned, but would not open her eyes, and then he laughed. 'What you swallowed, my dear, was only a powdered almond, not the pearl of Bahrain! See, here it is, that pearl of great beauty that you so coveted. Take it as a gift from me and let me see you smile again. Have it made into what you will, O Pearl of Pearls that you are!'

The Treasure Hoard of the Afreet

*I*N AFGHANISTAN, THE WINTERS ARE LONG and hard and the snow falls from the end of October until the beginning of March. It is then that the magnificent snow-leopards of the mountains enjoy life in the desolate ranges. Their thick, creamy-white mottled fur keeps them warm and the wild game falls easily to their clever hunting. They live like kings in splendour, all through the cold, chill wintertime.

One fine day long ago, when the snow lay deep on the ground and glassy icicles hung from the trees, a leopard hunter named Haidar made his way stealthily through a wooded thicket at the foot of the mountains, on the trail of a magnificent beast that he had been tracking for hours. He was one of the bravest and cleverest hunters in the whole of the God-gifted Kingdom. His elder brother was a renowned ibex hunter, and many fine scimitar-like horns decorated the walls of their father's house, which was built like a fort from strong walnut wood on the slopes of the mountain. Haidar's snow-leopard skins covered the floors of his mother's harem, and whenever either brother went on a hunt, each hoped to outdo the other. Several times that day Haidar had caught a glimpse of the snow-leopard he was trailing. Each time, just as he got his gun ready to fire, the handsome animal disappeared. But in the deep snow the animal's tracks were clearly visible.

Haidar went forward cautiously: there were some huge rocks nearby and he knew that the creature must have sought refuge in a crevice. There was a dark opening in the boulder-strewn slope which lay ahead as he came out of the thicket, and he crept closer and closer to it. Inside the cave there was a sweet smell such as a snow-leopard leave behind when marking its territory. With great care, Haidar inched along on his stomach like a caterpillar.

Finally, he entered and was surprised to find that he had stumbled upon — not a snow-leopard's lair — but a veritable treasure trove. As his eyes got used to the shadowy cave, he could see huge iron-bound chests, some with their heavy lids open to reveal strings of pearls, daggers and jewelled scabbards and every kind of gold ornament. Scarcely able to believe his eyes, Haidar forgot all about the leopard and, dropping his gun, picked up one glittering necklace after another, opened chest after chest, finding ever more beautiful objects inside them.

'Surely this must be the finest treasure in the world!' Haidar cried aloud, strings of rubies, pearls and diamonds dripping from his fingers. 'Who can be the owner of all this magnificence, I wonder?'

A voice issued from the depths of the cave, a voice which was loud and shrill: 'It belongs to me, wretched man! How dare you enter this cave of mine without my permission?' Lit as if by some magical power, a flame sprang up in the cave, blinding Haidar with its light and making all the jewels, golden bowls and vases gleam with a dazzling beauty. Haidar could see nothing but the flame in the middle of the cave floor, which grew brighter and brighter.

'Who are you?' he cried, looking about him and expecting to see a gigantic *afreet* or *jinn* which would seize him and crush him to death with an enormous club. 'I'm sorry, I did not mean to rob you, believe me, whoever you are! I came upon the cave by accident... I swear it! I just came in pursuit of a snow-leopard I have been following!'

A loud laugh came from the darkest part of the cave and, as the flames of the fire leapt higher and higher, Haidar could see a small evil spirit, an *afreet* approaching him, his tremendous eyes almost popping out of his completely bald head. He wore a coat and boots made of leather and, though small, he looked thoroughly evil, his face wreathed in an angry scowl.

'Wretched fellow!' screeched the *afreet*. 'That leopard is my own special pet. Had you harmed one hair of his pelt you would have paid for it with your life! He is my bodyguard — if you were to lay a finger upon me he would, at my command, tear you limb from limb!'

'No, no, I would not harm him, since he is your pet,' said Haidar as calmly as he could. His mind was telling him to turn and run, to get out of there as fast as his legs would carry him, but something kept him rooted to the spot as the *afreet* came nearer and nearer. 'I'll just take my gun and continue on my way,' he stammered.

The *afreet* became even angrier and, jumping up and down as if he were dancing a jig, he shouted, 'You cannot leave here now that you have discovered my treasure! You must stay and serve me. My last slave has just died so I have no servant to do my bidding — I will keep you here forever!' He picked up Haidar's musket and hurled it into the fire where it was soon consumed.

'Now follow me into the inner cave.' He stared up into Haidar's eyes, and in spite of his strong desire to run, Haidar found himself completely mesmerised, like a rabbit before a snake. He followed the *afreet* into an inner cave where flaming torches lit the walls. Another fire burned brightly and more torches lit up each corner.

The huge leopard, which Haidar had tracked to the cave, was

sitting on a mat beside the fire washing its beautiful mottled coat, as tame as any cat. But Haidar knew that at one word from its master he would have been killed by those flashing teeth. On one side of the cave, there was a bed of skins and the smoke of the fire went curling lazily out through a large hole in the roof of blackened rock, no doubt leading to a natural chimney in the mountainous slope outside.

The afreet told Haidar proudly, 'All the chests in this room are full of gold coins. Those baubles outside are mere rubbish compared with the riches I have in here!' and he pointed to numerous chests, securely padlocked with bolts of brass and copper which gleamed in the firelight. 'Now sit down there, slave, and I will give you your orders. You must go out and collect firewood for my fires, then you shall cook my food, and sweep the floor of the caves. Then, you will fetch snow in those buckets, and boil it so that I have water to fill these two barrels. You cannot escape for I have hypnotised you, slave, and you will do as I say. At night, you must sleep in a third cave, smaller than these two, where you will find a bed of skins. I will call you when I want you to bring me food and drink in the morning.'

Hypnotised by the *afreet*, Haidar did as he was told. A day and a night passed, with Haidar in a state of complete submission to the dreadful *afreet*. At night, as he lay on the floor of the smallest cave, Haidar could hear the *afreet* counting coins like a miser, hundreds upon hundreds of them, and laughing to himself with fiendish glee. Haidar reckoned that the situation in which he now found himself was hopeless: he could never escape and, after a few days, his family would give him up for dead, thinking that he had probably been killed by a wild animal or had fallen into a snow-pit.

But what the *afreet* had not told Haidar was that his hypnotic powers were only effective while he was awake. On the second night, Haidar cooked and served the evening meal, and ate a few mouthfuls himself. Then, when the fires had died down, he crept from his cave and listened. The evil *afreet* was sleeping deeply, snoring on his bed. Would the leopard attack if he tried to escape? Haidar knew he must make the effort to get away.

Summoning all his strength, he suddenly realised that he was freed from the *afreet's* hypnotic power, though in the day-time he could do nothing but what he was told. In the corner, the mat where the great snow-leopard usually slept near its master was empty. Haidar could see by the flickering light of the torches that he could escape — if only the *afreet* did not wake to turn those large, baleful eyes upon him and hypnotise him again.

Scarcely daring to breathe, he slowly pulled on his boots and made his way silently into the first cave. There was no sign of the snow-leopard. At last, he was on the threshold of the cave, of freedom. He sent up a fervent prayer for protection, and saw the moonlight shining on the snow outside. He could not resist taking one of the strings of priceless rubies as he crept out. What a souvenir of his dreadful experience this necklace would be! He knew that if he had nothing to show for it, no one would ever believe him. Also, he felt entitled to something in place of his gun, which the *afreet* had destroyed.

In the moonlight, he made his way to the thicket where he had first seen the snow-leopard, praying that now, without his gun, he would not meet any wild animal that night. It was a long way home but, with his hunter's instinct, Haidar knew how to avoid animals as well as to find them. There was still a dagger in his belt which might be useful if he met any creature face to face.

He hoped that he would not need it.

After the full moon's rays had lighted him part of the way, Haidar was so tired and cold that he climbed into the thick branches of a sprawling walnut tree and slept fitfully until dawn. Waking then, he pulled his fur-lined coat around him and smiled as he felt the smooth ruby beads in his pocket. What a wonderful present for his mother, but would she ever believe him? The vision of the evil *afreet* who had hypnotised him made him fearful for his safety, and he set off for home as fast as he could in case the horrible creature had sent the snow-leopard after him. The snow was beginning to fall heavily again when he arrived at his father's house at last, hungry and exhausted.

As he staggered through the doorway, frozen to the bone, the sight of the happy faces of his father and brother and his mother's tears of joy were all he needed to save himself from collapsing. They gave him hot soup and piled furs upon him, and made him sit by the fire as he told his story.

But he could see that they did not believe him and put his tale down to sheer imagination or perhaps light-headedness after being lost in the snow for such a long time. His mother was pleased with his gift of the ruby necklace, but the family thought it must have been dropped by some rich lady, maybe a long time ago, and found by Haidar while he sheltered in a cave during the snow-storm. They were grateful to Allah that he had returned; never mind that he was half-mad and full of imaginings, they said understandingly.

'Come with me,' protested Haidar to his brother, 'I will take you there, and you will see those chests of treasure for yourself. If we both went, you could kill the hellish creature, and I could shoot the leopard guarding him, and we could be the richest men in the world!'

His brother, the ibex-hunter, looked at him quizzically and gave a loud laugh. 'Haidar, you are out of your wits! I don't like the sound of the whole adventure. It is much too dangerous to get involved with what must certainly be an *afreet*. These devils take many forms. No, no, get it out of your head! But by all means, tell the story to our friends at the tea-house. I am sure you will have a most interested audience — it's one of the best hunters' tales I have ever heard!'

And as his brother had prophesied, Haidar's tale of the hypnotic *afreet* and the chests of treasure was heard, told and re-told, and there were many interested listeners. In fact it was said that many men went in search of the caves of Haidar's treasure, but no one ever found them. Haidar himself went several times in the same direction when hunting leopards, but he never could discover exactly where it was that he had entered the mysterious cave and fallen under the spell of the dreadful *afreet*. For the rest of his days, he always hoped that he would find those chests of pearls, jewelled daggers, golden ornaments and all the rest of that fabulous store, but he never did.

In time, everyone came to believe that the afreet was one of the minions of King Suleiman, son of David, and that no human being would ever be able to see that hidden store of treasure again. And they were right, for such a cave has not been found in Afghanistan to this day.

The Nagging Grandmother

*Y*AQUB WAS A BAKER who had his own business, inherited from his father, and he decided one day that he needed a wife. He was young and strong and made a good living, so the local match-maker had no trouble in finding him a pretty girl from among the daughters of local tradespeople.

At the wedding, the bride, whose name was Majeeda, was unhappy to find that she would not be mistress in her new home, for the baker's grandmother was still in residence. Yaqub's mother had died soon after his father and the old woman, who was a widow, stepped into her place, giving constant orders to the servant girl, and arranging what they were all going to eat each day. She always seemed to be finding fault with someone and she nagged Majeeda from morning till night, but never in front of her grandson — she was too cunning for that.

After just a few days in the baker's house, the bride hated her husband's grandmother so much that she had to put her fingers in her ears to avoid the sound of that nagging voice. Yaqub, of course, did not know how troublesome his grandmother was being, because he was busy baking at night and then selling the bread during the day. The first meal the bride made was quite all right in his eyes, but when the old woman tasted it she said 'Tsk! Tsk! Tsk!' and raised her eyes to the ceiling, slowly shaking her head from side to side. So Majeeda was not even allowed to cook the simplest dishes which she knew she could do quite well; she always gave in, allowing the bad-tempered old crone to dominate her.

One day, Majeeda went out to the bazaar to buy some material to make new curtains, and she returned with some fabric after striking a good bargain with the cloth merchant. When Majeeda asked her what she thought of it, the grandmother felt it once between finger and thumb and, shaking her head, declared only 'Tsk! Tsk! Tsk!'

In view of the grandmother's age, Majeeda did not like to complain to her husband, as he naturally paid her great deference. The old woman often told Yaqub that she was training his wife in the art of how to run a household. He believed her and told Majeeda that she was very lucky to have his grandmother to teach her and give her the benefit of a lifetime's experience.

Now Majeeda was a skillful embroideress. She had made many beautiful shirts for her father and brothers when she was at home, but her handiwork was not good enough for the baker's grandmother. 'What do you think of this linen shirt I am making for Yaqub?' she asked one day as she was carefully embroidering some delicate design all round the cuffs of her husband's new shirt. But she might have known not to ask such a question because, after examining it for a few moments, the old woman shook her head from side to side and emitted the usual 'Tsk! Tsk! Tsk!' Majeeda ran from the kitchen in tears and went to her room to cry alone. She put on her all-enveloping *chador*, and went to the house of her friend a few streets away.

'My dear, whatever is the matter?' cried that good woman. 'Has your husband been beating you? I always thought that he was such a nice, polite and kind young man! Tell me all about it.' And so Majeeda did.

'I cannot go on living under the same roof as that dreadful old creature,' she wept, 'I must go back to my father's house, for I can never do anything to please her, no matter how hard I try! Yaqub will never believe the truth about her because she never does it in front of him.'

'Now, now, don't worry any more!' said her friend, 'I know what you can do — you need the help of someone who is used to dealing with this sort of trouble. You must come with me. I will take you to visit Kuftara the witch. Everybody goes to her when they are in difficulties.' Together they went to a small house a little way away, and knocked on the door.

'Who is it?' cried a shrill voice, and Kuftara the witch looked out of the window. Seeing the two women with their faces unveiled, she recognised Majeeda's friend as an old client and opened the door at once. She had a long, thin face with big black eyes, snow-white hair and a long nose. There were rings on every finger and many silver talismans round her neck.

Majeeda poured out her story and begged the witch to help her. 'I will pay you anything you ask,' she cried, 'I have some money here...'

'Don't worry, my child, it will not cost you much,' was the kindly reply. 'I will look in my cupboard and find you something suitable for this case.' She turned away and rummaged in a wooden cupboard painted with curious birds and beasts.

'Ah, yes, here it is.' 'It' was a small bottle in which there was a greenish liquid. Her large black eyes were full of laughter, and she pushed the bottle into Majeeda's hand. 'Put this in the broth next time your husband's grandmother has a meal, and that will solve your problem — you will not have to worry about her ever again!'

Majeeda paid her what she asked, and they hurried away. 'I don't want to *kill* the old woman,' whispered Majeeda to her friend. 'After all, she is my husband's only living relative, and I would hate to have that on my conscience.' Her friend stopped her. 'No, no, my dear. Kuftara the witch would never poison anyone, she may just make a sort of — transformation. She has done some really wonderful things to help people in difficulties, and we always benefit from her actions!'

With her suspicions allayed, Majeeda went back to her house, and waited for the opportunity to administer the green liquid. She did not have long to wait, for the grandmother called to her from her upper room as soon as she saw Majeeda had returned:

'Wherever have you been all this time? Hurry and get me a bowl of that broth I made this afternoon. I am very hungry and my dear grandson will not be in till late tonight, so let me have it for my supper now!'

Majeeda put the pot containing the soup on a brazier and blew on the red hot charcoal to heat it, for she knew the grandmother liked it very hot. Then, with a quick movement, she emptied a small amount of the green liquid into it and took it upstairs to the old woman. 'Tsk! Tsk! Tsk!' she scolded Majeeda, 'why didn't you bring it sooner? Didn't I tell you I was very hungry? Go down again quickly and bring me some fresh bread to dunk in this soup — I made it myself from my own favourite recipe to be sure it would be all right. Now, don't stand there loitering, hurry back!' and she spooned some of the soup greedily into her toothless mouth.

Majeeda turned and ran down the narrow stairs, hastening to do the crone's bidding. How long would it take for the witch's brew to work whatever magic it was supposed to? She wondered what would happen, and what the consequences of putting it into the soup would be. She took one of her husband's fresh loaves from the bread barrel, broke off a piece and ran upstairs, hoping that the grandmother was not dead. If she were, Majeeda knew it would not be long before she was accused of the crime. But upstairs, there was no sign of Yaqub's grandmother. The bowl was empty and the spoon was lying on the carpet. Majeeda called out in a quavering voice, 'Grandmother! Grandmother! Where are you?' But there was no answer. No grandmother was to be seen in the bed or under it. Whatever could have happened? Had the old woman fallen out of the window? Had the frail wooden balcony given way? She rushed to the window and looked out. No, there was nothing but the usual street scene, with people strolling about and donkeys carrying firewood or parcels of goods to the market.

Majeeda closed the window and drew the curtains, taking the bowl and spoon down to the kitchen to wash them in time for her husband's evening meal. She threw away the small green bottle into the very furthest part of the garden, and washed her hands quickly in case any of the magic disappearing liquid had got onto her fingers. When her husband came in the soup was ready, and there was curd cheese and fresh bread on two plates.

'Where is Grandmother, my dear?' asked Yaqub, as he had a second bowl of soup. That evening, he was really secretly relieved that the talkative old crone was not in the kitchen, as he longed to be alone with his wife. Just lately he had begun to notice how much the old woman dominated Majeeda, and her constant fault-finding was beginning to get on his nerves. His grandmother had become so tiresome that he began to regret that she had not been taken away by the Angel of Death at the same time as his grandfather.

'I don't know where she is,' said Majeeda. 'I haven't seen her for hours,' which was perfectly true. She realised that the green liquid given to her by the witch had something to do with the old woman's disappearance, but she was not going to tell her husband about her visit to the witch with her friend. That would always be her secret.

Yaqub reported his grandmother's disappearance to the local police, but nobody ever saw her again. Superstitious neighbours supposed that she had been carried away by a *jinn*. After a while everybody forgot all about the vanished woman, and got on with living their own lives. The baker was happier than he had ever been, now that the two of them were together at last, in loving harmony.

But Majeeda knew what had happened. Often, a small green lizard sat on the bedroom balcony and, putting out its tongue, it would shake its head from side to side making a strange noise, 'Tsk! Tsk! Tsk!' before scuttling back into a hole in the wall.

The Girl with the Glass Heart

ONCE UPON A TIME in the old days of long ago, there lived a nobleman called Ahmad Khan. He had many acres of beautiful land, excellent riding horses, and four handsome sons. But the greatest joy in his life was his daughter, Shirin. He lavished so many presents upon her that she became petulant and conceited and nobody liked to be in her company.

Her mother told her that she was both selfish and vain, her nurse foretold an unhappy fate for her in life and her four brothers teased her unmercifully, all in order to try to reform her way of behaving. But every time she wanted something and it was refused her, she ran begging to her father, with her bewitching brown eyes. But she was not happy, for what human being is when the milk of human kindness is not in their breast?

One day, when Shirin was about seventeen years old, her father decided that it was time she had a husband. He sent messages to all his friends and his cousins over the mountains, inviting them to a great feast, and asking them to bring all their marriageable young sons with them. In time, they came and stayed for many days, feasting at Ahmad Khan's table, and shooting Ahmad Khan's partridges and hunting the ibex with him in his hills, knowing that soon one of them would find favour in his eyes as a suitable husband for his beloved daughter.

Shirin was as willful as ever when her mother told her that the suitors were being entertained.

'What are they to me?' she pouted, 'I have looked at them all as they feasted with my father and I don't like the appearance of any one of them!'

'My dear child,' said her mother. 'They are the finest and wealthiest young men in the country and all you have to do is choose one of them. As you say, you have seen them feasting with your father and riding out to hunt — each of them knows that you are to make up your mind about one of their number in the next few days.'

'Mother,' said Shirin impatiently, stamping her foot, 'I tell you I don't like one of them even the least little bit, and I wish that they would all go away and stop hoping!'

Shirin's mother was very annoyed with her and turned away in anger. A female servant approached her to ask about the preparation of the next meal, and they went off towards the kitchen together. The girl sat on a velvet pillow on the floor, agitatedly twitching at her long dark braids of hair. Why did they want to marry her off, she asked herself? Everything in life that she needed, she could get from her father, she knew that — why should that not go on forever? What need had she of a silly husband?

At that very instant, the room grew dark, and a slim, radiantly beautiful lady, dressed in fluttering garments of green silk sewn with emeralds, appeared before her. The lady said, in a voice that was like the sighing of the wind in the trees in spring, 'Shirin, Shirin, you must marry in order to make another person happy. You cannot and should not live all your life in your father's house. It is not right. You must begin a new life in your chosen husband's house.'

'What husband? Where is he? I don't see anyone I like!' said Shirin defiantly.

'Ah, then, my dear, you must be blind,' said the beautiful vision, 'for there is one out there, and one alone among the suitors, who loves you very dearly. He will give you everything that your father has given you (and more) and will eventually make you happier than you have ever been.'

Shirin got to her feet, and looked out of the window to where the radiant lady pointed. The room was dark, but out in the garden, picked out by the bright sunlight, stood a tall, handsome young man, in riding boots, leather breeches and a velvet coat embroidered with coloured silk. He wore a tall fur hat on his head, and was talking to a groom who had just brought him a large grey horse with a snow-white tail.

'That is your future husband, Shirin,' said the angelic personage, getting fainter. 'Be advised, my dear, that there is no one else in the world for you… make up your mind now, or lose your happiness forever.'

Then, as suddenly as she had materialised, she was gone.

The room grew brighter again, and when her mother came back Shirin was looking very thoughtful. She knew that some fairy had visited her, but she did not want to share the excitement of it with her mother. She looked out of the window again, but the handsome young man had ridden out of sight. She began to feel a faint flutter of interest in him, and the thought that he could give her more than her father had ever given her secretly thrilled her.

Next day, there was a huge gathering in the banqueting room, and she was standing veiled beside her mother, her aunts and cousins, supervising the massive meal as servants scurried hither and thither to put vast platters of spiced pilaus, skewered meats and delicious fruit before the men. Shirin watched the young man the fairy visitor had prophesied would be her husband.

The enamoured suitor ate all that was given him with every sign of enjoyment, and he smiled a good deal. She took stock of his features. He was well-built, but not bulky; his shoulders were broad but his body was well-proportioned. His eyes were large and kind, his nose was strong and like the beak of a hawk. His mouth was wide, and a smile was always playing about his lips. All his movements were quick and neat.

After the feast, the women sat down together and naturally discussed the suitors. When Shirin asked the name of the man the fairy had indicated was deeply in love with her, the answer was 'Nadir Jan'. Next day, when her father asked her which suitor she favoured as a husband, the answer was 'Nadir Jan'.

Ahmad Khan was delighted, for Nadir Jan was the one he would himself have chosen for his daughter. 'Shirin,' said he, 'light of my eyes, you have chosen well. You will be a happy wife, for Nadir Jan has kindness, good looks and an impeccable family history, similar to our own. Allah's Blessing upon you both. I shall get the marriage contract drawn up at once.'

A few weeks later, Shirin and Nadir Jan were married according to the law, and he took her home to his own lands to introduce her to his people.

At first, Shirin was as spoiled by her new in-laws as she had been by her father. But, after a month or two had passed, when she began again to be petulant and capricious, her husband said his first cross words to her.

'You are a married woman now, my dear,' he said severely. 'I think that you had better behave like one, and not like a vain, conceited little girl.' And he left the bedroom where Shirin was pouting at her mirror, turning her head with its delicate braids of long dark hair, this way and that. No sooner had he gone than the room became dark, and Shirin caught her breath, for there was the beautiful fairy again in her bright emerald-sewn green silk garments. She spoke in her strange voice, like the singing of the wind in early spring: 'My dear Shirin, you have become the wife of this handsome, charming young man just as I told you that you would. Why are you not happy? And why are you making your husband unhappy too? Tell me everything, and I will try to help you.'

Shirin turned from the contemplation of her own face and the feeling in her heart was very strange.

'I don't know why, but I cannot, just cannot feel any love for him!' she said, with a sob. 'I thought that he would do everything for me as my father had done and more, as you promised, but — but every time I try to feel happy, I am not.'

The enchanted being drew nearer and tapped Shirin on the breast with her long, shining silver wand. There was a faint 'ting' and the lady said, 'Oh, now I see what is wrong! Your heart is made of glass. No wonder you cannot feel anything for your husband. We shall have to do something about this, but I'm afraid it won't be easy to put things right.'

'My — my heart is made of glass? But — but how could that have happened? What is the meaning of a glass heart?' wept Shirin.

'Alas, we do not know,' was the softly spoken reply. 'Sometimes humans are given glass hearts, or glass hips, or glass minds, by the Evil Ones. They take away your own heart, especially if you look too often in the mirror. If you do not use your mind, they will take away your brain and give you a glass one. If you do not use your senses, they can give you glass hips, and no one can touch you without breaking you to bits! Many a husband has taken his wife to bed on the wedding night and heard nothing but 'ting' when he tried to embrace her.'

'How can I get my real heart back?' asked Shirin. 'I will do anything, anything you say, if I can be happy and feel love.'

'It will not be easy,' replied the radiant vision, and her voice was now quite sad. 'But if you do as I tell you — in time all may be well. You must give up every thought of new clothes, jewels, or vanities of any sort. You must not even speak to your husband, whatever he may say to you, for the space of three moons. You must wear the simplest clothes, do the same work that you expect the servants to do now, and give all your money to the poor. Your husband's wishes — his slightest whim — should be your commands. And if you can cast out all thoughts of greed, vanity and pride from that glass heart, it will break into a thousand pieces and disappear into nothingness. Your own heart will then return to you from wherever it may be hidden, and your life with your husband will be happy ever after.'

'But supposing that I cannot pass all these tests? What shall I do then?' cried Shirin.

With a smile sweeter than honey, the beautiful lady shook her head, waved her long silver wand, and vanished.

The room brightened again. Shirin put her looking glass away in her bedroom cupboard; she took off her long silken robes and put on the simplest clothes she possessed. All that day she worked with her servants in the house, helping them instead of demanding attention every few minutes.

In the evening, her husband returned home. It was easy not to speak, as he was not speaking to her. He averted his gaze most of the time, and busied himself cleaning his hunting knives. Next day, he rode away on his grey charger to a distant part of his domain with just a silent kiss on her brow as farewell. She made him a new suit of clothes, dying the cloth the deepest indigo blue, as she had seen her mother-in-law do the week before. Whenever her maids came to receive their orders, she just made signs, and they took the news to her in-laws that their young mistress had been struck dumb.

When her husband came home again, he appeared to be in a bad temper. He shouted at her several times while she was serving him his meal. His large, once-loving eyes were sad, his mouth no longer had an elusive and charming smile playing round it. The mother-in-law came in and whispered to her son that some evil spirit had taken away his wife's tongue! 'The girl is possessed by a *jinn*!' she muttered.

Whatever he said to her after his mother had gone to her own room, Shirin pretended not to hear, so that he began to imagine that she had also become deaf. She sat beside him with lowered eyes in her plain clothes, feeling nothing in her glass heart, neither love nor hate — only a great emptiness in her breast.

But she remembered the fairy's warning that it was not going to be easy, so she bided her time. By the coming of the next moon, she was beginning to enjoy the various tasks around the house. In the garden, she saw for the first time the beauty which comes out of the black earth every Spring, in the form of flowers and grass, and she heard with ever-quickening interest, the song of birds outside her window as she sewed and stitched at her husband's clothes. Her mother-in-law shouted at her as if she were deaf, but she bore the noise in her ears patiently and waited for time to pass. When two moons had come and gone, she was so helpful and kind to others that her husband began to feel his old love for her returning.

His heart went out to her— she had been apparently struck dumb and deaf and he decided that he would search for a doctor to cure her and restore her speech and hearing. His mother said that it was a hopeless case, and that she would never be right again. She even hinted that her daughter-in-law had some mental derangement, but Nadir Jan felt he must at least try. So he got the name of a doctor in a far-away land who was supposed to be a miraculous healer of the deaf and dumb. It took him the space of about one moon to settle his affairs, and then he was ready to go.

He dressed in travelling clothes, and sent for the grey charger. He would go on the immensely long and difficult journey in search of the great man, in the hope of persuading him to return with him and help Shirin with her problems. When she saw that Nadir Jan was about to leave, and learned from what he said to his mother that he was about to make such a dangerous journey on her behalf, something seemed to flutter in her mind. As he swung his leg over the saddle she reached out her arms to him. Something also started to flutter in her breast — she did not know what it was. She clung to her husband's stirrups, and, to everyone's surprise, she found her voice and cried, 'Nadir Jan! Nadir Jan! Don't go! I love you!'

With a shout of joy, Nadir Jan leapt from the saddle and crushed her in his arms. 'A miracle!' he shouted. 'My wife is well again, she can speak, she can speak!' He carried her back into the house, sending the grey horse back to the stables with the groom. Then Shirin told him everything about the radiant lady, and they both realised that the glass heart had broken into thousands of fragments at last, and that her own heart had returned from wherever it had been hidden by the Evil Ones.

Shirin fell deeply in love with her husband at the time of the third moon, and from that moment on he never ceased to love and honour her.

The Keeper of the King's Horses

ONCE UPON A TIME, many ages ago, there lived a powerful and arrogant King. He owned great palaces, and ships carried rich merchandise from far-away kingdoms to supply him with all the treasures of the then-known world. Hundreds of beautiful mares and stallions from the finest bloodlines were kept in his stables. His mighty army was feared by his enemies and, in every corner of his dominions, his justice was known to be swift by all those who had done wrong. His messengers brought him news from everywhere, going as far as the borders of China in the East, and his name was feared even by the kings of Roum in the West.

Those were the days of bows and arrows, and when he went hunting he made sure that his weapons were always finer than those of his attendants, whatever their rank.

One day, to rest from the affairs of state and the ostentatious ceremonies of the court, where ambassadors from other countries came with messages from other kings, he went off hunting — this time alone — for he wished, just for once, to forget that he was a King at all.

Deeper and deeper into the forest he went, without even a page to carry his arrows, in search of such game as might be found in the deepest part of the wilderness. He was only thinking of the chase; his mind was alert and he felt at peace with the world. Once or twice he sighted an animal, a fine golden hind, but each time he fitted an arrow to his bow she moved quickly into the undergrowth, and he lost sight of her.

He glimpsed her again, but she vanished once more, protected by her natural camouflage among the trees of the forest.

Like his father before him, the King was a good huntsman, but he finally realised that he had lost the hind despite all his years of experience. In some annoyance, the King threw himself down at the foot of an ancient tree to rest. 'Perhaps my eyes are tired,' he thought to himself. 'I will give them a chance to recover for a while before I start again.'

Suddenly, he was startled by the sound of a dry twig breaking and looked up to see an old man standing within a few feet of him.

Fearing that the man was either a robber or an assassin, the royal hunter quickly fitted an arrow to his bow and cried, 'Who are you and what do you want? Come a step nearer and you will be a dead man!'

The aged man knelt before him and, with a calm face in which shone a pair of faded, guileless eyes, said, 'May you live forever, O Most Auspicious Monarch! Allah's Peace be upon you, your Majesty! I am Hamid Khan, the keeper of your Majesty's horses. I know the name of every one of the animals under my care, their sires and their dams, and the foals still at foot. Yet you, you recognise a hind in the forest more readily than the face of one of your oldest subjects!'

At that, the King felt deep shame. He laid down his bow and his face flushed. He raised the old man, and asked to be forgiven for his thoughtlessness. They returned to the palace together, the contrite King conversing with the old man all the way, all thoughts of the chase forgotten. He realised that never before had he spoken to old Hamid Khan, though he had been Keeper of the King's Horses for so many years.

From that day forward the once-proud ruler resolved to get to know his subjects better, no matter how lowly their occupations, and he took every opportunity to build bridges between himself and them. He realised, now more than ever, how dependent he was upon them and their loyalty, and one of his responsibilities was to know each one of his subjects as well as the horse-master knew his horses. Allah sent him many years of peace from that day onwards, when he had come to fuller understanding of the importance of thinking of others as well as himself.

The Magic Talisman

ONCE, LONG AGO, A WEALTHY MAN called Wali Khan was hunting one day in some woods at the very edge of a great ravine, when he saw a small girl collecting nuts. She was a very pretty child, but dressed so poorly that he stopped and gave her a coin to spend in the market.

'Thank you, good sir,' she said. 'I have no need of money, for I live by eating the berries and nuts of this wood. I would not know where to go to spend it, anyway, for I have never seen a market-place.'

'That is remarkable,' said the surprised Wali Khan. 'How long have you been here and how did you come to this wood, which is so remote from humankind?'

'I was stolen from my home far away — just how far I do not know — by nomads who carried me off whilst I was playing with my sisters in the garden of our home,' she replied. 'They camped on the edge of the ravine one night and in the morning I was able to escape from them. After they had gone I found berries and nuts and drank the water from the falls dripping from yonder rocks. Soon I must be on my way to see if I can find my home, because I am very lonely here, with only animals for company. The nomads may come back this way and I fear they may catch me again.' She began to cry.

Wali Khan wiped her eyes and said kindly,' My dear child, I will take you back to my house. There you will be cared for by my family until such time as we can discover where your own people are, and you shall be as one of my daughters, who are about your age.'

He picked her up and sat her on his shoulder and carried her to his large house. His children came running out, clamouring to know who the girl was. She told them her name was Qubilah, that she was eight years old and that she had three sisters.

Wali Khan took the child in to his wife and soon Qubilah was washed and dressed in clean clothes, enjoying a game with the other children. In the course of the next few months, Wali Khan sent his messengers out in all directions, seeking information about any family which had recently lost a little girl called Qubilah, who had been carried off by nomads. Sadly, no information about her home came to light anywhere.

After a while, Qubilah began to feel at home with her new family and the images of her father and mother, her old home and sisters, gradually faded from her mind. So the years passed, and there came a time when she forgot the earlier part of her life. Wali Khan's wife became her mother, and taught her all the things that the daughter of such a household should know. She learned to spin wool from a sheep's fleece, to weave, to embroider with silks, and to cook the most delicious dishes.

Her seventeenth birthday was celebrated joyfully by her adoptive parents. It meant that she was of marriageable age and they would soon begin to look for a husband for her. Wali Khan's three daughters grew jealous of her around this time, because she had grown beautiful and clever and they felt she outshone them in everything she did. Qubilah was not aware of their resentment towards her; she was a sweet-natured person herself and never bore anyone a grudge.

The very next day, a prince came riding past with all his attendants, and whom should he see in the garden but Qubilah, cutting roses for her room. On an impulse he stopped his horse, and telling his retainers to wait, knocked on the door to ask for a drink of water.

This was, of course, merely a pretext to find out who the beautiful girl was, and whether there was a chance of speaking to her. He was looking for a bride — his father had told him only that morning that it was time he was married. When the servant brought the young prince, whose name was Sadiq, into Wali Khan's presence, they liked one another, and Wali Khan was very pleased to have such a splendid visitor to entertain. He called for refreshment for the whole retinue, as well as the finest food for his guest.

Qubilah, meanwhile, had noticed the noble young man with her father, as she came into the house with the roses, though she pretended not to be interested. But when she ran upstairs her cheeks were bright pink, for she had fallen in love with Prince Sadiq at first sight.

At the end of the meal, the young man asked Wali Khan: 'Please do not think me a man without honour because of what I am about to say, but believe me, I ask this from the bottom of my heart... May I marry your daughter?' Wali Khan was very surprised, and said: 'I have four girls in my family. Which one do you mean, and how is it that you have made up your mind so quickly?'

'I cannot say, except that it is the one who was gathering roses in your garden as I rode past. I fell in love the moment I looked at her,' he replied. 'All my life, I have always made up my mind quickly. Please give your consent, good sir, and let me be the happiest man on earth!'

Wali Khan smiled, and said, 'Well, that would be Qubilah and I will ask her whether she is willing.'

So Qubilah was sent for, and when she came downstairs and shyly said she would marry him, the young prince was the happiest man alive. The prince rode away to tell his father he had found a bride and Qubilah ran to tell her sisters of her good fortune. Though they pretended to be very pleased, the three girls were more jealous than ever, and they complained to their mother that it was not fair that the foundling, as they now unkindly called her, should be married before them.

'Who is she, anyway?' said one, 'Found by our father, tattered and torn, in the middle of a wood?' 'Yes,' agreed another, 'she may have been telling him a pack of lies. She is probably a nomad whose family deliberately left her behind as she was only a girl!' This and other vicious remarks were made by Wali Khan's daughters, who now hated her even more than they had done before.

Qubilah had no inkling of this but lived in the happiest state imaginable, preparing her wedding clothes and waiting for Prince Sadiq to return for her. At last he came back, with a great number of nobles and servants, to escort her to the palace which was his home. Wali Khan rode proudly beside the carriage with four fine horses which the prince had sent to take her, her adoptive mother and the three discontented sisters to the wedding.

The marriage took place at the Amir's palace, amid much excitement and ceremony, and Qubilah was welcomed with joy by all the royal family. The wedding party was to last for seven days and seven nights. Both Sadiq and Qubilah found that they were as much in love as any young couple had ever been since the beginning of time, and they looked forward to a long life together.

The courtiers, however, were soon aware of the fact that Qubilah had been found in a wild wood, wandering about eating berries and nuts, and without a family background suitable for the bride of their prince. This was, of course, because of the malicious whispers circulated by the three daughters of Wali Khan, who were determined to wreck the happiness of the girl they had now decided was nothing better than a gypsy. The Amir's wife sent for the three girls, and asked them for the truth about the new bride's history. 'We thought that she was the daughter of our honoured subject, Wali Khan,' she said severely. 'What is this I hear, that my son Sadiq has been tricked into marrying a poor gypsy girl, found in the wood dressed in rags and eating nuts and berries?'

The three mischief-makers stammered out, one by one, that the story was true, and called upon Allah to witness that they spoke no lie. Convinced by this, the royal lady dismissed them and asked a maidservant to bring Qubilah to her immediately.

Dressed in her beautiful silk garments, with new gold earrings and her long dark hair braided with strings of pearls, Qubilah came happily to her new mother-in-law, expecting some charming discussion about where her new apartments were to be. Imagine her dismay when the first thing she saw on the royal lady's face was a frown, and no welcome in her eyes. Qubilah's blood grew chill, and she asked, 'Why did you send for me? What has displeased you so?'

'I have heard that you are not of good birth, that you were brought back by Wali Khan from a hunting trip in some forsaken region, and that there is no known history of your ancestry! What sort of mother could one such as you be for the children of my son Sadiq? I always thought that he was too hasty in deciding to marry you, falling in love with a girl he saw gathering roses in a garden. I am very distressed at this news, and I do not know how I can tell this to the Amir!' cried the enraged Queen.

Qubilah, her eyes brimming with tears, went down on her knees and sobbed:

'Yes, yes, I realise that I am not good enough to be your son's wife, but please believe that we love each other, and I will try to make him happy. Do not send me away from Sadiq, I beg you!'

'I'm afraid that for the good of our family, you must go back to Wali Khan's house. I will ask my son to choose one of his real daughters for his bride. It was far too hasty a choice, and it has always been said that if marriage is embarked upon hastily, it is repented at leisure. I do not blame you, my dear girl, of course it is not your fault, and I know that Sadiq is in love with you.' A smile came to the older woman's lips, 'I really felt that you were suitable when I first saw you, but... but...' Suddenly she stopped and caught at a silver ornament which Qubilah had hanging round her neck, on a leather thong. 'Where did you get this? It is a talisman that once belonged to someone who was very dear to me. How did you come into possession of it? Tell me at once!'

'I have had it round my neck since I was a child,' replied Qubilah. 'When I was kidnapped from my home by the nomads, I was wearing it, and I have worn it ever since,' she went on, wiping her eyes. 'I remember that my mother put it round my neck when I was very young, telling me that it would keep me safe from all harm, for on it was inscribed the Throne Verse from the Koran.'

'I gave it to your mother! I would know that talisman anywhere,' sobbed her mother-in-law. 'Oh, my dear, my dear, forgive my cruel words just now. I wish I had seen it earlier — you must know now that your mother was the Lady Laila, a dear friend of mine with whom I used to play long ago before she went to be married to your father. Ah, poor girl, poor girl! Only recently, I heard the sad news that she and your father were killed by a band of robbers in their palace only twenty miles from here. I knew that the greatest sadness in their lives was that some nine years ago their little daughter was stolen from them by a thieving nomad band who carried her off while she and her three sisters were playing in the garden.'

'Then… then I am of good family after all, and a suitable bride for my prince?' asked Qubilah, fingering the silver talisman which had been her lucky charm all her life.

'Yes,' came the reply. 'I ask you to forgive me for what I said, my dear girl, and I thank Allah for sending me the daughter of my dearest friend to be the wife of my son. Your three real sisters are married to fine husbands, with homes of their own in a part of the country which is not far from here, so I will arrange for you to meet them as soon as that can be managed. Your parents are dead, alas, but I will take your dear mother's place, for her sake,' and Qubilah felt a pair of warm, loving arms around her.

Joy shone in Qubilah's eyes once more and she hastened away to bathe her eyes and calm her nerves, before going to tell her new husband that he had three sisters-in-law of her blood as well as the daughters of Wali Khan. And with grateful fingers, she touched again the magic talisman hanging round her neck and blessed its power.

In time, when Qubilah had found husbands for her adoptive sisters, they became friendly towards her and happy in their own lives at last. When her three real sisters and she were re-united after so many years of separation, Qubilah's cup of joy was full, and in time Allah sent her and Prince Sadiq many sons.

The Game of 'I Remember'

THERE WAS ONCE A YOUNG COUPLE who lived on a farm. They were happy and contented all day long, so well did they get on together.

The husband, Abdul Rahim, was a man who liked a joke, and one day he said to his wife, Bilqis, 'Let us play the old game of "I Remember" which my grandmother taught me; it will enliven our days.'

'I do not know it,' said Bilqis. 'Tell me what we have to do to play it.'

'Did your mother never teach you the game?' said Abdul Rahim, in surprise. 'It goes like this: two people agree that each will say "I remember" every time the other one hands them something. Then if one of them forgets to say "I remember", they have to pay a forfeit, which they decide in advance.

'I shall ask you for a new silver necklace, the best that the jeweller has in the bazaar!' cried Bilqis merrily, and Abdul Rahim agreed.

From that day forward, whatever it was that was handed to her, Bilqis immediately said, 'I remember' as she took it, and her husband did the same. They had many a laugh playing the game, and so clever were they, and so determined was each to keep the other from winning, that it went on for about six months. Had Bilqis forgotten to say the magic words, she was to give Abdul Rahim a new embroidered waistcoat, and each of them was determined to win.

The days went by, and work of the farm proceeded as usual.

The days grew hot, and then the days grew cold, and Abdul Rahim decided that he would go to the distant town to get seeds and new supplies that were required before the long winter set in. Bilqis's married sister and brother-in-law came to stay, to help out on the farm and to keep her company while he was away; also, Bilqis was expecting their first child.

As they waved him on his way, the last thing he did was to pass his wife a small purse of money containing the wages for the ploughboy, who was soon to return to his own village until spring. With a happy smile, Bilqis took it and said, 'I remember!' adding smartly, 'You won't get that embroidered waistcoat from me this time!'

The snow began to fall much earlier than usual that winter. It snowed and snowed, and snowed and snowed, until many roads were blocked, including the road to Abdul Rahim's farm. He was going to be delayed for several weeks longer than he had expected. Although he was a good climber, he decided that it was best not to go on any further in such bad weather, for travellers were often caught in whirling blizzards in that part of Afghanistan. So he turned back. He stayed with the owner of the nearest tea-house until the danger was past, and eventually was able to struggle back to his farm. The sunlight shone on the glistening snow as the heavily-laden farmer returned. The smoke from the fire inside was rising into the sky as he pushed open the door, stamping his feet to get the caked snow from his boots. His wife was sitting beside the fire in the low chair which he had made for her in the early spring. He had been anxious about her, as he knew her time must be near. To his great joy, the infant, wrapped tightly in its swaddling-clothes, was on her lap. Bilqis looked up at Abdul Rahim, her face wreathed in smiles, pink as a peach in her excitement.

'Abdul Rahim,' she murmured, 'here is your son,' and she proudly held the small bundle out to him.

He took the baby in his arms and gazed into the tiny face, the emotion welling in his heart. The small mortal looked back at him with a steady gaze.

He did not speak, but his wife did. 'My husband,' she murmured, and her voice had a triumphant ring to it, 'may I remind you that you have forgotten to say "I remember". Therefore I claim the silver necklace which I have won at last!'

Abdul Rahim was so pleased that he did not mind at all, but he and his wife decided that now that they had a child they would have no time to play silly games. And while she was rocking the baby in its walnut cradle, Bilqis made him a beautiful embroidered waistcoat after all.

The Carpet Merchant's Daughter
and the Snake

*I*N KABUL, THERE ONCE LIVED a carpet merchant called Abdul Salam, his wife and their daughter Niloufer. When Niloufer was about seven years old, her mother fell ill and died.

As Niloufer was an only child, and she reminded him of his wife, Abdul Salam spoiled her in every way. He was always buying pretty things for her and indulging her slightest whim. The servants in the house grew tired of pandering to her and left her more and more to her own devices. This continued until one night, when all the servants were out at a wedding feast, thieves broke in and stole everything that was of value. Since the servants never came back, the merchant suspected that they must have been in league with the robbers.

Niloufer and her father found themselves quite alone in the virtually empty house. After a great deal of thought, Abdul Salam decided to go to his brother in Kandahar and see if he could lend him enough money to buy more goods, or give him some carpets to sell, for he was too proud to ask his friends in Kabul for assistance. Before he left, he asked the neighbours to look after Niloufer for a short time, until he got back from his journey, and he gave them half of the money he had left to pay for her food.

Naturally Niloufer felt very sad and lonely when her father went, for there was no one to spoil her now. From being the apple of her father's eye, she was now poor and unwanted. At first, the woman in the house next door fed her like her own children, but then, as the money Abdul Salam had left was used up, she gave her less and less.

The other children began to taunt her, telling her that her father was never coming back. Each day she looked out of the garden gate to see if her father was coming up the road, but he did not come. She cried herself to sleep at night, wondering if she would ever see him again and if he had ever loved her at all.

One day, she decided to run away and look for her father. She took a cotton bag and filled it with walnuts from the big tree in the garden where she used to play so happily and, before dawn, she set off down the road. She walked and walked and, when the sun rose, she sat down beside a stream. She washed her face and hands, drank the delicious water and ate some walnuts. The sun grew hotter and hotter and her feet hurt, but she began walking again. She met people going into Kabul, on horseback, or leading strings of pack-camels, but they did not take any notice of her.

Two nomad boys came towards her with a sack, which had something wriggling about inside. Laughing and shouting as children will, they hooked the sack over one of the branches of a tree and gave it a few thumps with a stick. Then, ignoring Niloufer completely, they ran off, hopping and whooping, after some goats. Niloufer wondered whatever could be in the sack which was swinging and wriggling wildly. She was afraid that it was full of imps and was terrified of going near it. She was just about to take to her heels when she heard a strange voice coming from the sack, calling to her, 'Save me! Save me! Untie the sack and set me free and you will be rewarded! I can see you through a small hole, little girl. Help me, please! Untie the sack!'

Standing on tiptoe and pulling at the sack, she just managed to get it off the branch, and untied the string round the top. Out slithered a long, shiny, green and brown snake covered with lustrous scales. It had glittering, black eyes and its long, forked tongue flickered at her.

'How is it that you are able to speak? I do hope you are not going to bite me,' cried Niloufer in a fright.

'No, no, my child,' replied the snake, 'I certainly will not harm you! I promised to reward you and I will keep my word. Say what it is you want and it shall be yours.'

Niloufer said that the only thing she wished for at that moment was a pomegranate and a glass of sweet mulberry sherbet. In the blink of an eye, she had the pomegranate in one hand and the glass of delicious sherbet in the other. She looked at the snake in amazement. It was curled up on the ground before her, its tongue flickering in the sun. She drank the sherbet to the last drop and gratefully peeled the pomegranate, thanking the snake between bites of the fleshy seeds.

'Where are you going?' asked the snake, and she told it the story of her escape from the neighbour's house to try and find her father.

'But did he not tell you to wait for him till he returned? What will he think if he gets home and you are not where he expects you to be?' said the snake with its bright, unwavering stare.

'I cannot wait any longer. I know I can find him if I look on the road to Kandahar,' said Niloufer eagerly.

'You will never get to Kandahar on foot, with no one to guide you. You don't know how far it is, and you don't know the direction,' the snake hissed sharply. 'Now let me hang around your neck, and I shall tell you how to get to my master's house. He is a famous snake-master, and he will reward you for saving my life.'

So Niloufer put the snake round her neck, and was surprised to find that it felt as sleek and soft as the silver necklace her mother used to wear. She was quite happy to carry the snake that way and was not afraid of it any more. She picked up her cotton bag filled with walnuts, and followed the snake's directions. As they journeyed, the snake told her that it had the magic power to grant wishes for others but not for itself, which was why it could not free itself when it was captured and tied up in the sack by the nomad boys.

'I was lying sleeping on a stone in the sun, when those young rascals captured me,' said the snake. 'I do not know what would have happened to me if you had not rescued me. But I see that you are getting tired, for you are stumbling. Why do we not ride?' and in a trice a beautiful little donkey-cart appeared in the middle of the road. As if in a dream, Niloufer got into the cart, with the snake still round her neck. Soon she was laughing happily as she held the reins of the long-eared donkey and her sore feet felt better again. The snake called out to the donkey, 'Take us as fast as you can to the house of my master, for this young lady must find her father and I know my master will help her.' So off they went, bowling merrily along.

In no time at all the cart arrived at the gate of a large, white-walled house, set among mulberry trees and others laden with walnuts as big as the ones which grew in her own garden in Kabul. It was a very beautiful scene, but Niloufer began to feel nervous. 'Who *is* your master?' she asked the snake, as she descended from the cart. 'This big house must belong to someone very important.'

'Calm yourself, my child,' said the snake. 'My master is a kind and wonderful man who has a great reputation in the world of magical things which are beyond the comprehension of ordinary beings. He is the Lord of many snakes, and there are hundreds of us under his command. Sit here, under these trees, beside the fountains, and I will go and tell him of your arrival, and how you rescued me.'

So Niloufer took the snake from round her neck and laid it on the ground, while she looked about her at the beautiful garden. The snake slid away and she sat on a cool marble seat behind which there was a rose bower laden with delicately scented pink blooms. The sun had lost its fierce heat, and the whole garden was pleasantly warm and comforting, as she imagined the gardens of Paradise must be. Could it all be a dream? Would she waken to find herself back in her neighbour's home? She rubbed her eyes, but the scene around her did not fade.

Some time later, the grand carved door of the house opened and the green and brown snake glided towards her on the coloured mosaic pathway. Behind the snake walked the tallest man Niloufer had ever seen. His eyes were pale grey with dark pupils; his hair, under a small, round embroidered cap, was as white as silver, and he wore a long-sleeved, padded multicoloured silk coat which reached to the ground.

Niloufer jumped up from her marble seat and tried to speak, but could find nothing to say. So she stood still and cast down her eyes, very aware of her dusty, tattered clothes, trying to stop the fluttering of her heart. The tall man soon put her at her ease. He motioned to her to sit on the marble seat again and took a chair beside her with a charming smile; Niloufer found herself smiling too when she looked up at his calm face.

The snake coiled itself round one of the legs of its master's chair, its lidless eyes glittering.

'You have done me a great service.' said the snake master, 'you saved the life of my favourite snake, after those unfeeling children had tied it up in a sack and beaten it with a stick. Do they not realise that snakes are Allah's creatures, just as we are? I am very grateful to you for what you have done, and I hope that I can reward you in some way which will be of use to you. Please tell me if you will, now that you are sitting here in my garden as an honoured guest, what I can do to help you.'

Niloufer's nervousness vanished as she listened to the old man, for she realised that he was a powerful magician, and would be able to find her father. She told him her troubles from beginning to end, and when she had finished, he said: 'Tomorrow I will send all my snakes to every part of Kandahar where merchants gather, and by tomorrow night you will know where your father is now and what his present condition is. Now, my snake will take you to that part of the house where my wife and daughters can entertain you, and you may stay with them as long as you like, until your father can come to fetch you, if Allah wills!' With that, he got up, and went back the way he had come.

The snake uncoiled itself from the chair-leg and glided towards another entrance, telling Niloufer to follow. A maid-servant opened a latticed door, and Niloufer saw a beautiful room, covered with the rose-coloured carpets of Turkistan, and lit by many miniature lamps of pale blue glass hanging from the ceiling. The snake-master's wife, a tall lady with a sweet face, wearing a rainbow silk robe and golden jewellery, was beckoning to her to enter, and the snake slid away. She bade Niloufer welcome and told her she would go and find some clothes for her.

Then four beautiful girls appeared, telling her that they were the tall lady's daughters. They helped her to remove her torn clothes and bathed her in water scented with jasmine and rose oil, after which she felt reborn. It was many a day since poor Niloufer had seen such luxury, and when a maid-servant dressed her in the clothes which the Snake Master's wife had sent her, she felt like a princess. The women of the house feasted together as night fell, and they all clamoured to hear Niloufer's story from beginning to end. That night she slept between silken sheets in a room into which the moon shone with pale, brilliant light. She did not stir till the morning sun touched her face with golden fingers. At first, it all seemed still to be a dream; then the promise of the Snake Master came back to her. That evening, when the snakes had brought their reports back to their master, she would know about her father.

She sat in the rose-bower in the garden with her new friends, the daughters of the house, waiting for the Snake Master to send for her. At about midday, the green and brown snake came to her and said, 'Follow me, there is news of your father.' It led her to a study lined with manuscripts and books of great antiquity.

'Come in, daughter,' said the tall old man, 'I hope you are rested? My snakes have spent all night gliding along balconies, peering through windows, and creeping in and out of holes in walls. They have brought information that your father is in a town not far from here with a caravan of camels which he has borrowed from your uncle. He should be passing here this very day on the way to Kabul, ready to start his business again, and he will be expecting to find you awaiting him, my child. Prosperity will be with your father soon.'

Niloufer began to cry with happiness on hearing that her father was indeed alive and well, and with the merchandise to become as successful as he had been before once more. Suddenly she was afraid again, and asked, 'Oh, good Snake Master, how can I get back to our old house so that I can be there when he arrives in Kabul? I see now that I should never have run away. If it had not been for your snake, I might have perished on the road!'

'Do not fear,' the old man told her soothingly, 'a magic carpet which I keep for special occasions is ready to take you home, just as soon as you have said your farewells to my wife and daughters. But one thing I require of you, that you do not tell anyone of this adventure of yours, nor of the existence of myself or my house.' After promising never to tell, Niloufer kissed his hand in respect, and thanked him from the bottom of her heart. She then ran to thank the ladies of the harem for their hospitality and her new clothes, and sat in the garden to await the arrival of the magic carpet. 'Take me round your neck again, on the journey back to your home,' said the green and brown snake, 'for I will have to tell the carpet where to take you.'

The magical carpet, woven of every colour of the rainbow, appeared at Niloufer's feet and she sat down on it cross-legged, with the snake around her neck. Up, up, into the sky they flew, and Niloufer saw below her a long line of camels laden with merchandise on their journey back to Kabul, no doubt with her father riding on horseback somewhere in the caravan. She knew that it was he, and the snake agreed with her that it must be so, but she also knew she could never tell of the wonderful experience she had had since leaving home. Soon the carpet set her down in her own dear, deserted garden. As she slid the snake from her neck and placed it tenderly in the centre of the carpet, she felt a lump in her throat at having to part with the magical creature.

'Goodbye, and may you be happy always,' were the snake's last words to her as the carpet rose into the sky again. Niloufer waved a tearful farewell, and then she realised that she was once more wearing her old tattered clothes, and had her worn brown sandals on her feet instead of the golden slippers which the lady in the harem of the Snake Master had given her. Then she realised too that it was all for the best, for otherwise how was she to explain new clothes to her father and the neighbour next door?

At that moment she heard a loud banging on the front door of the house, and ran from the garden to find that her father had arrived at last. A servant was holding his new pony, and a line of camels were having their loads loosened in preparation for stacking them in the yard. Laughing and hugging her, Abdul Salam told his daughter that their troubles were now over, as his brother had given him plenty of merchandise with which to start all over again. New servants had also arrived from her uncle's home, he continued, so that she would once more be his spoiled child, his little princess, and he would never leave her again.

Soon the new servants were preparing a delicious meal, and Niloufer was able to put on a silken tunic and wide satin trousers which Abdul Salam had brought her from Kandahar. From that day onwards she was much more helpful and kind to others, forsaking her spoilt and capricious manner and leaving it behind in the time when she ran away from home and met the green and brown snake. Some people say it was a *jinn* sent by Suleiman to teach her consideration for others.

Abdul Karim's Escape

*I*N THE EVERLASTING SNOWS of the Himalayan mountains, overlooking the valley of the great Buddhas of Bamian, there lived a happy brigand called Abdul Karim. His home was in a cave of his own finding which he had furnished to his own liking. And his only close friend was his horse.

The horse was a fine black mare, her forehead decorated with a white blaze like the seal of Suleiman. They lived in perfect harmony — harmony such as he had never found with any female member of the human race.

The brigand galloped here and there to relieve some fat moneylender of a portion of his gold, or to help himself from the overloaded saddlebag of the last camel on the very end of a long caravan, as it snaked its way through the pass on the road from Bamian to Jalalabad. He filled his life with adventure, and found sufficient funds to keep his beloved horse and himself in the style to which they had become happily accustomed.

Somehow, without causing too much trouble to the upholders of the law in those parts, Abdul Karim very skillfully managed to escape capture and imprisonment. Loss of liberty would have been the death of his spirit, and he had vowed never to sacrifice his personal freedom. The bazaars and tea houses were buzzing with tales of his exploits and secret visits to lonely ladies whose husbands were far away; or comely widows who were seeking once more the joys of married bliss — adventures from which he always managed to extricate himself just in time. Maidens who were under their father's, uncle's or brothers' protection he left severely alone.

On the evening of which we speak, he was sitting by his fire roasting himself a delicious piece of meat, thinking of nothing in particular. His horse, which was standing tethered in the shelter of some trees, suddenly gave a nervous whinny and was answered by a similar cry. Abdul Karim started forward, meat in hand, and was startled to see another horse with a shrouded figure on its back. A scowl crossed his bearded face. His hand went to his knife and he shouted, 'Who are you? Stop, by Allah, or I will let you feel this.'

The veiled rider stopped, slipped from the saddle and ran towards him saying, 'Oh Abdul Karim, Abdul Karim, do you not recognise me? I am Zenab of the house of Iskandar Gul, the Amir's Master of Horse. He has been away from home, buying *buz kashi* mares and stallions from the tribes of the outlying provinces for these past three months. Remember our happy hours together when he was away before? I have decided to join you up here and look after you for the rest of your days, since you have no wife.'

Thunderstruck by this calamity, Abdul Karim cried, 'By my soul, lady, I really do not think you are in your right mind. Have some of this meat and *naan* with me for I am starving. It's a nice piece of mutton from a recently killed sheep. When you have eaten, I'll take you home. You should not be out here in these hills at this time of night. You might meet dangerous people.'

Zenab swayed towards the brigand and sat down on the rock indicated as a seat. Taking the meat on the skewer to the flames again, she sizzled it to a perfect kebab. 'I will never return to my husband. He's hopeless,' she cried. 'Let me stay here with you.'

Abdul Karim's heart did not warm towards her. Something in the back of his mind told him that this woman was trouble. He munched silently at his own skewer of meat.

She went on, 'I will get this dreadful old cave really nice and tidy for you. I will send home for my favourite cushions and sheep-skin rugs, silken sheets for us to sleep in and padded bedcovers for the cold nights. We'll have Bokhara hangings on the walls, and a cook to make proper pilaus for you and sweet-meats — not this disgusting peasant food. You will see. It will be a paradise for two. You can go about your briganding, or whatever it is you usually do, but I'll be here every night to await your return, feed you and keep you happy until morning.'

Abdul Karim winced, finished his meal, wiped his hands on his beard and got up. 'Come, I'm taking you back to your home,' he barked. 'In this cave, woman, my word is law. If someone does not obey me, I'll give them a taste of this.' And he took down off the wall a long rawhide whip which he lashed several times in the darkness outside the cave.

The fire flared up. His eyes were blazing with rage. 'That ought to get rid of her,' he thought.

'Oh,' murmured the lady Zenab, clasping her long slim, bejewelled fingers together, 'you're so handsome when you're angry.' She sighed. 'Never fear, I will make you truly domesticated, however long it takes me.'

'Come,' said Abdul Karim gruffly. 'Get on your horse. I'm off now to rob a caravan and there may be shooting, so pull that veil right over your face. If you're going to share my life, you'll have to help me kill someone, anyone who's likely to try to kill me. Hurry, woman, we have no time to lose. We must attack the fat jewel merchants of Samarkand before the sun comes up. Get on your horse, quickly.'

He stuck two more daggers in his belt as well as a heavy, ugly looking pistol. He stamped out the fire, and poured water on it from a leather bottle. He pulled the lady Zenab to her feet, tugging her riding cloak around her. She shrank from him for the first time. Surely, this was not the famous romantic brigand living so unhappily alone in this exotic cave without the refining influence of female company.

Abdul Karim cleared his throat noisily and spat into the bushes. Zenab winced again. He heaved her onto her saddle, thrust her little boots into the stirrups and leaped onto his own mare. The moon had now risen full and round, illuminating the hill paths, the towering rocks and away in the distance.

'Go ahead of me,' grunted the brigand, indicating the path. 'Hurry! The rest of my band will be meeting me at the bend in the road down there on the valley floor. When clouds cover the face of the moon there will be quite a lot of killing, and much loot for all of us before morning...' He gave a long, blood-curdling laugh. 'If you don't know how to cut a throat effectively now, you'll soon learn the trade.'

Zenab looked around wildly, urging her horse in front of his. She was a good rider and was looking for her chance. As they rode along, taking care to avoid falling into the abyss below, Zenab recognized a road she knew and nudged her mare quickly forward. The moon showed her the way home and she took it. Her head down, knees digging into the horse's sides, her hands tightly clutching the reins, the lady Zenab was soon flying like the wind, as if the devil Shaitan himself were after her.

'Hey, there, where're you going?' bellowed the brigand with all the harshness he could muster. 'You don't know where the rendezvous is, only I know where to go. Come back! Don't you hear me?'

Zenab galloped on until she was nearly out of sight, and even then she did not turn her head as she disappeared from view.

Abdul Karim checked his mount and, looking up at the moon as if to share the joke, laughed his wild, free hillsman's laugh. Then he turned and his mare took him back the way they had come. Arriving at the cave he dismounted, rubbed the animal down and threw a blanket over her. With a light step he walked into his cave, lay down on his mattress bedroll, yawned, and stretched out. Clouds covered the fair face of the moon. His features relaxed. What an escape he had had. He had nearly lost his liberty. Never again, by Allah, Abdul Karim told himself.

Another happy, peaceful night. Soon, snoring heavily as was his wont, the sleeping brigand was blissfully unconscious at last, dreaming of his horse and himself galloping across the fair land of Afghanistan, the God-given kingdom of free men.